2X w

BIG BOOK OF
THANKSGIVING ENTERTAINMENTS

BIG BOOK
OF THANKSGIVING
ENTERTAINMENTS

A Collection of Original Plays, Poems, and
Novelties Written Especially for This Book
by Lenore K. Dolan, Noel Flaurier, and Others

BECKLEY-CARDY COMPANY
CHICAGO

FOREWORD

THE PLAYS, POEMS, AND NOVELTIES included in this volume are here published for the first time. They offer a selection of material which will meet the needs of the teacher or program director who is seeking a balanced Thanksgiving program with the expenditure of a minimum of time and effort.

The plays are varied in type, in length, and in number of characters. The poems represent all shades of Thanksgiving sentiment. The novelties consist of dramatic sketches, simple exercises, dances, drills, and songs.

There are selections suitable for all ages from little tots to young people. Among these selections will be found numbers appropriate not only for school entertainments, but also for church programs, club meetings, and other community gatherings.

The occasional musical selections suggested for use with some of the plays and novelties may be found in collections of songs commonly used for group singing.

CONTENTS

PLAYS

POEMS

NOVELTIES

Number of characters to be determined by director

PLAYS

OUR PILGRIM FATHERS

TIME OF PLAYING: *About twenty minutes*

CHARACTERS

ELDER BREWSTER, *a Pilgrim leader*

WILLIAM BRADFORD, *a very dignified appearing
   young man*

MRS. MULLENS, *a Pilgrim woman*

PRISCILLA, *as a child* [Act I]

PRISCILLA, *as a young woman* [Act II]

JOHN CRACKSTON, *a boy about eight years old*

JAMES CHILTON }
JOHN ROBINSON } *followers of* ELDER BREWSTER

ENGLISH SOLDIER

FOUR PILGRIM WOMEN

TWO DUTCH GIRLS

TWO DUTCH BOYS

DUTCH MEN *and* WOMEN, *any number*

MILES STANDISH, *the Captain*

JOHN ALDEN, *a young man*

TWO SAILORS

MASSASOIT, *the Indian Chief*

OTHER INDIANS

Any number of additional PILGRIM MEN, WOMEN,
   and CHILDREN

3

COSTUMES

ELDER BREWSTER: *Typical Pilgrim costume [knee trousers, buckles on shoes, etc.], with long black coat.*

OTHER PILGRIM MEN *and* BOYS: *Typical Pilgrim dress.*

PILGRIM WOMEN *and* GIRLS: *Older* WOMEN *wear dull-colored dresses with long sleeves and long, full skirts.* GIRLS *and young* WOMEN *wear dresses that are a little more brightly colored.*

DUTCH MEN, WOMEN, *and* CHILDREN: *Typical Dutch dress.*

MILES STANDISH: *Military costume with iron breastplate and helmet. The breastplate and helmet may be made by covering cardboard with metallic paper. Sword hanging at his side. Carries a heavy musket.*

ENGLISH SOLDIER: *Bright-colored cape thrown back over shoulder. Short, full breeches. Helmet and breastplate. Sword at his side.*

SAILORS: *Short trousers and old torn blouses.*

MASSASOIT: *Feathered headdress. Typical Indian clothing, which is elaborately decorated.*

OTHER INDIANS: *Typical Indian dress.*

ACT I: SCENE I

SCENE: *In the Brewster home at Scrooby, England. A plain stage with a few chairs and with two doors will suffice. When the curtain rises,* WILLIAM BRADFORD,

JOHN ROBINSON, MRS. MULLENS, PRISCILLA, JAMES CHILTON, JOHN CRACKSTON, *and any number of additional* PILGRIMS *are on the stage. Some are seated and some are standing, while* ELDER BREWSTER *is standing at one side of the stage speaking to them. They appear to be very earnestly listening to him.* [MILES STANDISH *and* JOHN ALDEN *are not in the group as they were not members of the group at this time.*]

ELDER BREWSTER. My dear friends, our meeting tonight is a very important one, for a few of us have been talking together and we have decided that since there is no place in the town of Scrooby—nay, none in the whole of Nottingham nor the whole of England—where we can worship God as we feel we should and must, it is our duty to leave this country and go to a place where we shall be free to do as our conscience tells us. [*Pauses and looks about.* PILGRIMS *look very much surprised as they turn and say a few words to each other.*] There is scarcely one of us who hasn't felt the strong hand of the law in punishment for our worship. We have been put in prison, we have paid heavy fines, and we have had our means of livelihood taken from us. I believe that we should take a bold step forward and go to a land where we can be free and our children can be free.

WILLIAM BRADFORD [*rising*]. You are right, Elder Brewster. We are not slaves but free Englishmen. We do not believe in the Church of England. According to our belief, religion should be a simpler thing, and it is our duty to protect our belief.

ELDER BREWSTER. You are right, William Bradford.

JOHN ROBINSON. I have been your faithful follower in all you have ever said, Elder Brewster, and if we go to a free place to worship I shall lead your church as sure as my name is John Robinson.

MRS. MULLENS. But where can we go? My husband and I and Priscilla would be willing to do anything in order to worship God as we wish.

ELDER BREWSTER. In the little country of Holland people are allowed to worship as they please, and I have heard that the Dutch people are very kind. If we could but reach there safely, I believe we could make our living and gain our freedom of worship.

JAMES CHILTON. There is nothing that stout hearts cannot do as long as it is for the cause of right and in the name of God. Let us leave England as soon as we can.

WILLIAM BRADFORD. Well spoken, James Chilton. We shall see about getting a ship ready within a fortnight.

JOHN CRACKSTON [*speaking to* PRISCILLA]. Then when we are grown up we shall not have the trouble our fathers and mothers have in worshiping God, Priscilla.

PRISCILLA. I hope that we won't, John Crackston. What fun it will be to sail away on a ship!

MRS. MULLENS. Hush, children, we must not be heard talking so loudly. Never speak of our leaving the country or the soldiers will put a stop to it.

[A *loud knock is heard at left door.* ALL *stop speaking and are perfectly still.*]

ELDER BREWSTER [*in a stage whisper*]. It's the soldiers! Come out this way and they will not see you.

[BREWSTER *points to door at right.* ALL *but* BREWSTER *leave quietly by the door indicated while the knock is repeated, louder each time. When they are off stage* BREWSTER *opens the door.* SOLDIER *enters.*]

SOLDIER. Brewster, why isn't your door open to a soldier of the law; and who was doing the talking I heard here?

ELDER BREWSTER. There is no one here, Sir.

SOLDIER. I can see that for myself now, but there was someone here and I know who it was. Some of those wretched Separatists have been meeting here again. The next time I find anything like this you are going to prison. There is no room in the town of Scrooby for any but loyal members of the Church of England. Do you understand?

ELDER BREWSTER. Yes, sir.

SOLDIER. Then remember it or you'll be in prison or worse. [*Exits.*]

ELDER BREWSTER. My heart is full of wrath at his words but it is better for our cause that I say nothing. I trust he may never have cause of complaint against me in this country again.

CURTAIN

SCENE II

SCENE: *In Holland. Two widths of wrapping paper may be extended across the back of stage and on this may be drawn in colored chalk Dutch windmills, cows, flowers, etc. Four or more* PILGRIM WOMEN *are at the side of the stage.*

FIRST PILGRIM WOMAN. It doesn't seem possible that it is almost twelve years since we left our homes in England and came to Holland.

SECOND PILGRIM WOMAN. We have fared well here, but there is one thing that I regret. The good Dutch people have taken us in as their own and our children are becoming more like the Dutch than like the children of England. While we love these good Dutch friends, we do not want our children to grow away from the English ways.

THIRD PILGRIM WOMAN. The Dutch are a good people

but they believe in more gaiety than we do. See those Dutch children now!

[*Enter* Two Dutch Boys *and* Two Dutch Girls *laughing or singing. They do a Dutch dance. At the close of the dance,* Dutch Women *and* Men *enter.*]

Dutch Woman. Children, children, come away. Our friends do not care to see you laughing and dancing in the street like this.

[*Exit* Children *and* Dutch Women.]

Fourth Pilgrim Woman. How carefree they are! It is well that our men are planning to go to a new country where our children can better be taught the seriousness of life.

First Pilgrim Woman. Do you really believe they mean to go off to this wild America? We know nothing of fighting such wild creatures as they say live there.

Second Pilgrim Woman. They say Miles Standish, our friend the soldier, has promised to go with us. I am sure he would be a great help to us.

[*Exit* All, *talking over the matter.*]

CURTAIN

Act II: Scene I

Scene: *On board the "Mayflower." Again the plain stage will suffice. However, the deck of the "May-flower" may be represented by a railing and some paper sails. A paper background may be used. Blue waves with a bright sunset lighting them may be drawn on the paper.* MILES STANDISH, ELDER BREWSTER, MRS. MULLENS, PRISCILLA, WILLIAM BRADFORD, JAMES CHILTON, *and other* PILGRIMS *are on stage.*

[*Enter* FIRST SAILOR]

MILES STANDISH. Well, sailor, can you tell me how much longer we should be on board ship?

FIRST SAILOR. Probably as long as we live, at the rate we are going. We have been on this wretched ship now for six weeks, and there is no sign of land yet. I wish we had never started out.

MRS. MULLENS. It is hard, but it is no harder on you than on the women and children, and we are not complaining.

[*Exit* SAILOR.]

ELDER BREWSTER. There is a difference between his case and ours, Mrs. Mullens. He is making the voyage because of the money he is to receive, and we are making it to serve God better. Because of our cause the Lord puts courage in our hearts.

WILLIAM BRADFORD. We have needed the help of God to keep alive for six weeks on this ship "Mayflower" for, though a good little ship she is, we are very crowded and the food is none too plentiful. If the other ship, the "Speedwell," had not leaked and had to be turned back, we would have had more room and comfort.

JAMES CHILTON. We must not complain. We must trust
God to bring us to a safe landing.

[*Enter* SECOND SAILOR]

SECOND SAILOR. From my reckoning we are well over half-
way to America. I believe that in a little over two weeks,
if conditions remain good, we shall be there.

PILGRIMS. Thank the good Lord for his kindness to us.
May we reach the land of freedom safely.

CURTAIN

SCENE II

SCENE: *An out-of-door place in the village of Plymouth
on the first Thanksgiving. The out-of-doors may be
represented by a number of branches placed about the
stage. Tables well filled with baskets and dishes are
at one side of the stage and near these the* PILGRIM
WOMEN *and* CHILDREN *are working. The* PILGRIM
MEN *enter with baskets of nuts, etc.*

ELDER BREWSTER. Our friends, the Indians, are coming
now to the Thanksgiving feast. I hope they will be
pleased with it and that they will continue to be our
friends.

WILLIAM BRADFORD. It is far better and safer to have them
for friends instead of enemies. That is one of the things
we can be thankful for on this Thanksgiving Day.

FIRST PILGRIM WOMAN.   I am so glad we thought of having this day of thanks. We have had hard times but the Lord has been good in giving us such a fine crop this year. It is fitting that we should thank Him for it.

JOHN ALDEN. I am very glad now that I came with you to this country, for I believe we are going to have the feast of a lifetime here today.

SECOND PILGRIM WOMAN. Yes, but John Alden, I believe you see more than this feast that pleases you greatly in our village. What do you think, Priscilla?

PRISCILLA. I have been too busy preparing this feast to notice anything for the week past.

[OTHERS *laugh.*]

PILGRIM CHILDREN. Here are the Indians.

[*Enter* INDIANS *with* MASSASOIT *ahead.* ELDER BREWSTER, WILLIAM BRADFORD, *and one or two other* PILGRIM MEN *advance and welcome them.*]

ELDER BREWSTER. Welcome, red men. Welcome to our first Thanksgiving feast.

MASSASOIT. Ugh! [*Points to* WOMEN.] Paleface squaw. [*Points to* CHILDREN, *who step away.*] Paleface papoose.

WILLIAM BRADFORD. Come, the feast is ready. We will all thank God together for the blessings he has given us all. May he keep us in peace and plenty for the year to come.

[ALL *move toward the tables as the curtain falls.*]

THANKSGIVING EVE IN THE CORNFIELD

Time of Playing: *About twenty minutes*

CHARACTERS

Field Mouse, *a small child*

Two Cornstalks, *tall boys*

Four Pumpkins, *small children*

Brown Squirrel, *a child somewhat larger than the one representing* Field Mouse

Four Scarecrows, *larger boys*

Harvest Moon, *a tall girl*

Six Moonbeams, *little girls*

Additional Pumpkins, Scarecrows, *and* Moonbeams *may be included if desired*

COSTUMES

Field Mouse: *Gray pajama suit. Tight-fitting cap with ears attached.*

Cornstalks: *A number of cornstalks fastened to clothes. Each boy carries a good-sized bundle of cornstalks in front of himself to hide from view his face and head.*

Pumpkins: *Each wears a little green cap and has a very large cardboard pumpkin attached to the front and back of suit or dress.*

Brown Squirrel: *Brown pajama suit with bushy tail*

13

*attached. A well-stuffed brown stocking with plenty
of cornsilks attached will serve as a tail.*

SCARECROWS: *Ragged scarecrow clothes.*

HARVEST MOON: *Bright yellow-orange dress. Holds a
large cardboard moon in front of herself.*

MOONBEAMS: *Fluffy white dresses with yellow sashes.*

SCENE: *A cornfield. Cornstalks and pumpkins placed
wherever space permits. A large moon suspended
over the stage by fine wire. [This should be pulled off
stage when* HARVEST MOON *makes her appearance
on stage.]*

When the curtain rises, the TWO CORNSTALKS *and*
FOUR PUMPKINS *are scattered about the stage. They
should remain very still until time for them to speak.*
FIELD MOUSE *runs in from side and goes near center
front of stage.*

FIELD MOUSE [*pretending to nibble something on the
floor*]. Nibble, nibble, nibble. My, but I am hungry!
[*Runs toward* FIRST CORNSTALK.] I think I will crawl up
that cornstalk and find a few kernels of nice corn for my
supper.

FIRST CORNSTALK. Oh, you do, do you, Mr. Field Mouse!
Suppose I do not care to have you taking some of my
corn for your supper.

FIELD MOUSE. Surely you will not care if I take only a few

kernels. I haven't had a bite to eat the whole long day.

SECOND CORNSTALK. I will tell you what we will do, Mr. Field Mouse. We will give you all the corn you can eat if you will tell us what is going on in the world outside of this cornfield.

FIRST CORNSTALK. Yes, tell us all the things you have seen in your travels, Mr. Field Mouse. You know we cornstalks never get out of this field so we are always glad to hear the news.

FIELD MOUSE. I will tell you about my trip to the farmhouse this afternoon. Everything there was excitement. The ladies were baking and cooking and the men were bringing in wood for the great fire. The fowl were in the oven, and the children were cracking nuts and popping corn.

SECOND CORNSTALK. Why were they all so busy? There must be someone's birthday near at hand.

FIELD MOUSE. No, it is not in honor of any birthday they are making such preparations. Tomorrow is Thanksgiving Day.

FIRST CORNSTALK. Thanksgiving Day! What is Thanksgiving?

FIELD MOUSE. I am sure I don't know. I was frightened away by the family cat just as they started talking about what a great day it was.

SECOND CORNSTALK. I wonder who could tell us about it,

It is very provoking to know there is such a great day
in the world and then not to know what it is about.

FIELD MOUSE. I've told you all I know about the day.
Now I will take the corn for my supper.

[FIELD MOUSE *runs behind a shock of cornstalks.*]

FIRST CORNSTALK. I wonder if there isn't someone else
who could tell us about this great day. I am very
anxious to hear more of it now.

SECOND CORNSTALK. Here comes Brown Squirrel. He
ought to know what is going on in the big house for he
often goes there to watch the children at play.

FIRST CORNSTALK. Oh, Mr. Brown Squirrel, do you know
anything about Thanksgiving Day?

SQUIRREL. Do I know anything about Thanksgiving Day?
Ho, ho, ho, but that makes me laugh! Of course, I
know all about Thanksgiving, and everyone in this cornfield ought to know all about it, too.

SECOND CORNSTALK. We never heard of such a day until
a few minutes ago. Why should we know all about it?

SQUIRREL. You should know about Thanksgiving Day
because that day is set aside to thank God for His goodness in allowing you to grow and produce a bountiful
crop. The great day started years ago when a field like
yours produced enough food one fall to supply a little
band of settlers with food for the winter. Without

such fields as this there would never have been a Thanksgiving Day. Now don't you think you ought to know all about it?

[SQUIRREL *scampers behind a bundle of cornstalks.*]

FIRST CORNSTALK. I never knew there was a day set aside in our honor. We must be more important than we think we are. Here's a group of jolly pumpkin heads. I wonder if they know anything about Thanksgiving.

[PUMPKINS *jump up and move about stage. They then come to center front of stage, where they sing the following to the tune of* "Tramp, Tramp, Tramp."]

1. In the cornfield big and broad
   We have chosen to make our home,
   And we think it is a very pretty place.
   To grow big and round we try,
   To be ready for a pie;
   To be the largest pumpkin each does race.

CHORUS

Cheer, cheer, cheer for jolly cornfields!
That's where we like best to be;
But when Thanksgiving time is here
We will all be picked, I fear,
And pumpkin pie upon each plate you'll see,

2. When Thanksgiving time is near
All the woods are brown and sere,
But the pumpkins bear their shiny, yellow glow;
And we brighten up the way
On that joyous festal day
By filling that delightful pie that you all know.

CHORUS

[*When the* PUMPKINS *finish their song they scatter about the stage.*]

SECOND CORNSTALK. Oh, then you pumpkins do know about Thanksgiving. You mentioned it in your song.

FIRST CORNSTALK. We just heard about the day a little while ago. Won't you tell us all about the day?

FIRST PUMPKIN. Ho, ho, ho; so you cornstalks don't know about Thanksgiving Day. Why, I wouldn't think the world was worth living in if it wasn't for that day.

SECOND PUMPKIN. We furnish all the pies for the Thanksgiving Day dinner. If it wasn't for Thanksgiving I am afraid a lot of us pumpkins would go to waste.

FIRST CORNSTALK. Who started this great holiday? Has it always been celebrated in the world?

THIRD PUMPKIN. There have been harvest festivals observed for many hundreds of years but the real Thanksgiving Day started in America more than three hundred years ago.

SECOND CORNSTALK. Who started the holiday in America?

FOURTH PUMPKIN. We would really like to tell you all about it, but you see the cook is looking for us now so we must hurry on. It must be frightfully dull to have to stay in this stupid old cornfield on Thanksgiving Eve.

[*The* PUMPKINS *run off stage.*]

FIRST CORNSTALK. It is all right for those pumpkins to speak lightly of the cornfield now, but when this same field was supplying their vines with food and water that was a different matter.

SECOND CORNSTALK. I wonder who will tell us more about this Thanksgiving Day. The people must do more on that day than just eat a great dinner.

[*Enter* SCARECROWS. *Come to center of stage and sing to the tune of* "Old Black Joe."]

1. Gone are the days when we scarecrows were in use;
Since our prime's past we suffer sad abuse.
Gone are the crows and the fields are brown and sere,
I hear the night winds calling, "Thanksgiving Day is here."

CHORUS

We're happy; we're happy,
'Cause we've done our work right well,
And all about Thanksgiving we'll gladly tell.

2. Gone are the shoots we watched with greatest care;
Gone are the tasseling stalks so green and fair.
Autumn has stamped her colors bright and clear.
I hear the night winds calling, "Thanksgiving Day
   is here."

CHORUS

[SCARECROWS *walk limply around stage and stand
near* CORNSTALKS.]

SCARECROWS [*in unison*]. We know about Thanksgiving
Day. It is a day on which to be thankful for all the
blessings that have been received throughout the year.

FIRST SCARECROW. You may wonder what a scarecrow
would have to be thankful for, but I assure you there are
a great many things for which we are grateful. There are
some people who think they have to have everything
they desire before they have cause to be grateful, but we
do not belong to that group.

SECOND SCARECROW. Our clothes may be ragged and old
and our joints may be loose, but that doesn't stop us
from being thankful for the happy summer we have
had in God's great out-of-doors.

FIRST CORNSTALK. I wish we could go to a house some-
where and take part in a Thanksgiving celebration. I
think that would be fine fun.

SECOND CORNSTALK. There is no use wishing for such a

thing for you know we can't leave this field until Farmer Brown hauls us away in his wagon, and he will never bother doing that when there is a holiday at hand.

THIRD SCARECROW.   You do not need to go to the big house to have a Thanksgiving celebration.   A cornfield is the finest place in the world to have one.

FIRST CORNSTALK.   But who could we have for our guests? I am sure that where they have such feasts there must be lots of fine guests.

FOURTH SCARECROW.   We will all be your guests and perhaps there are others who would like to come if they heard about it.

CORNSTALKS.   Hurrah!   Hurrah!   We will have a real Thanksgiving party right here in the cornfield!

[*Enter* HARVEST MOON. *Bows to* CORNSTALKS.]

HARVEST MOON.   If you gentlemen are looking for guests for your Thanksgiving party, I can name some delightful little folks who would be very glad to come.

FIRST CORNSTALK.   Why, if it isn't Harvest Moon!

SECOND CORNSTALK.   I always thought that there was a man in the moon, but now I see it is a delightful young lady.

HARVEST MOON.   I overheard you talking about guests for your Thanksgiving party so I dropped down to tell you that my little moonbeams would be glad to come and join you.

FIRST CORNSTALK. That will be fine. We shall be delighted to have them.

SECOND CORNSTALK. The moonbeams will feel at home here for they come to this field to play nearly every evening.

HARVEST MOON. Then I will tell them of your kind invitation. I am sure they will be delighted.

FIRST CORNSTALK. We would like to have you with us, too, Harvest Moon.

HARVEST MOON. Really, I am such a busy person that I couldn't think of spending so much time away from my moon castle. The moonbeams will tell me all about your good time when they return home. [*Turns toward the audience and recites the following.*]

> High above you, Harvest Moon
> Rides alone in her delight,
> Lighting up the world below
> On each gay autumnal night.
> On each field and wood and lake
> Softly falls that lovely glow;
> The beauty of that Harvest Moon
> All people love and know.
>
> High above you, Harvest Moon
> Travels all the world around,

Shedding rays of light and joy
On each countryside and town.
Now that Thanksgiving's pleasures
Have descended on us all
Harvest Moon renews her splendor
And lets her choicest radiance fall.

[HARVEST MOON *bows and glides off stage as* MOON-
BEAMS *dance onto stage. They dance about before coming to front of stage, where they sing the following to
the tune of the chorus of* "Dixie."]

Oh, I'm glad it is Thanksgiving!
Hooray! Hooray!
The time of feasts and jollity,
The time of fun and company!
Hooray! Hooray! Hooray for gay Thanksgiving!
Hooray! Hooray! Hooray for gay Thanksgiving!

FIRST CORNSTALK. We didn't expect you moonbeams so
soon. You must have hurried right down here.

FIRST MOONBEAM. We did. You see, we moonbeams
cannot be out after the sun shines so we thought perhaps you would hold your Thanksgiving party now.

SECOND MOONBEAM. We would be very happy if you
would, for we have never really been at a Thanksgiving
celebration although we have peeped in at them quite
often.

SECOND CORNSTALK. We shall be glad to have our feast
now if it will please such lovely creatures as you. I am
sure the others will be willing.

[*All characters that have been hidden by cornstalks
or have gone off stage step into view.*]

FIELD MOUSE. Yes, yes; let's have our party now. I always
feel safer in the moonlight than I do in the daytime.

SQUIRREL. So do I. Tomorrow there will be so many
hunters in the fields and woods that I won't dare to put
my head out.

FIRST SCARECROW. It will please us all right. We look
much nicer in the moonlight than we do in the bright
sunshine.

FIRST CORNSTALK. Then we will start our festivities right
away. How glad we are to have learned about Thanksgiving Day.

SECOND CORNSTALK. We will have the moonbeams dance
for us. Then we will have a merry Thanksgiving party
in the cornfield until morning. Will you dance for us
now, moonbeams?

MOONBEAMS. We will be glad to.

[*To any gay tune the* MOONBEAMS *give a short dance.*]

CURTAIN

WHY BE THANKFUL?

TIME OF PLAYING: *About ten minutes*

CHARACTERS

MRS. MASON

BERT, *her son*   CARL, *a neighbor boy*
ANN, *her daughter*   STELLA, *a neighbor girl*

COSTUMES

MRS. MASON: *A house dress and an apron.*

BERT, ANN, CARL, *and* STELLA: *Ordinary clothing.*

SCENE: *A living room. Doors at right and left. Window at back. Furnishings as desired. Papers on floor. At the rise of the curtain,* MRS. MASON, *with a spoon in her hand, hurries into the room.*

MRS. MASON [*calling*]. Bert! Where are you, Bert?

BERT [*offstage*]. I'm out here. [*Enters.*] What do you want?

MRS. MASON. I want you to go out and get some red leaves and other decorations for our Thanksgiving dinner.

BERT [*sourly*]. What are we going to do—eat the leaves? I thought we were to have turkey.

MRS. MASON. No, we're not going to eat the leaves. They're to trim the table. It's a wonder you wouldn't

25

take some interest in Thanksgiving Day. [*Picks up papers from floor.*]

BERT. I might take some interest if you'd buy me that football you've been promising me for a million years.

MRS. MASON. Are you still harping on that?

BERT. Yes, I'm just like an elephant. I never forget. [*Sinks into a chair and begins fixing his knife.*]

MRS. MASON. What? Sitting down already?

BERT. Sure! I need my knife if I'm going to cut leaves— and my knife has a loose blade. I'm fixing it.

MRS. MASON. Hurry up, then. And while you're sitting there just try to be a little bit thankful.

BERT [*leans back languidly*]. Why be thankful—when I haven't any football?

[*Exit* MRS. MASON. *Enter* ANN, *carrying several books.*]

ANN. Oh, here you are, Bert. I've been looking for you. I want you to take these books to Jimmy when you go past his house today.

BERT [*stops working on his knife and frowns*]. What kind of nonsense is this? If Jimmy wants the books, let him come and get them.

ANN. But he can't. He broke his leg yesterday. Where have you been, anyway, that you don't know?

[BERT *looks up in amazement.*]

BERT. Broke his leg! [*Whistles.*] Jiminy crickets!

ANN. Yes, broke his leg—and these are some of the Ted Hanover Adventure Books, which he likes so much. Will you take them over to him?

BERT. Sure I will. Well, if that isn't bad luck. I'm thankful I—[*Stops short.*] No, I'm not.

ANN. What are you talking about?

BERT. I almost said I was thankful, but I still don't have any football. [*Gets busy on his knife.*]

ANN. You are stubborn. [*Looks out window.*] There comes your pal, Carl.

BERT. Wonder what he wants.

ANN. I don't know. I'm waiting for Stella to come. We have to make plans for the school party next week.

[*Doorbell rings.*]

BERT. Let him in, Ann.

[ANN *goes to door.*]

CARL. Hello, Bert. I'll bet you're surprised to see me.

BERT. I am kind of surprised. Anything happen?

[*Exit* ANN.]

CARL. Plenty. We have to get another fellow to take Richard's place when we make our trip up to the hunting lodge on top of the hill.

BERT. Why? What's wrong with Richard?

CARL. Nothing wrong with him. But there's been some kind of accident in his aunt's family over at Greenville. His mother has gone over to Greenville, and Richard has to stay at home for a few days to take care of the baby.

BERT [*scandalized*]. Take care of the baby? How's he going to do that?

CARL. Oh, bounce her on his knee, and that sort of thing.

BERT. Bounce her on his knee! Good night. Well, I certainly am thankful—[*Stops and frowns.*] No! I'm not. I'm not thankful at all.

CARL [*sighing blissfully*]. I am. What a job!

[*Enter* ANN *with* STELLA.]

ANN. I think pumpkins would be nice for the trimmings, don't you, Stella?

STELLA. Yes, I do. Pumpkins and Pilgrims cut out and pinned all over everything—the curtains and the walls and all.

ANN. Did you see Grace Martin, Stella? She's on the committee.

STELLA. Yes, I did. She isn't coming to the party. Do you know why? She can't afford to bring anything for the lunch because they're so poor.

ANN. Oh, how dreadful!

STELLA. They live in such an old house. I went there the other day. And Thanksgiving dinner isn't even mentioned.

CARL. Gosh! I never thought to look at Grace that her folks were that hard up. I feel sorry for her.

BERT. Thanksgiving dinner never even mentioned! What do you know about that?

[*Enter* MRS. MASON.]

CARL. Think of having no turkey and no pumpkin pie.

BERT. I sure am thankful—[*Stops, then speaks with emphasis.*] Yes, I am. I mean it. I'm thankful through and through. [*Jumps up.*]

MRS. MASON [*amazed*]. What in the world has happened?

BERT. Imagine whining about a football—with all the good luck I have. A fine home, good health, and right this minute a twenty-pound turkey cooking in the oven.

MRS. MASON. That's the way to talk!

BERT [*grabbing cap*]. Come on, Carl! We'll cut leaves and all kinds of fancy boughs. We'll make this house look like the forest itself.

ANN [*with enthusiasm*]. It's great to be alive—in America. I'm thankful for that.

STELLA. It's wonderful to celebrate Thanksgiving Day. I'm thankful we have such a day.

BERT. I'm thankful for everything—no broken legs, no bouncing the baby, no empty cupboard. Thanks, I say. And I also say—I was a plain everyday grouch. Come on, Carl. We have work to do!

[BERT *and* CARL *go out the door.*]

CURTAIN

INDIAN SUMMER LEGENDS

TIME OF PLAYING: *About fifteen minutes*

[*Any parts of this number may be selected for presentation if a shorter number is desired.*]

CHARACTERS

STORYTELLER [OKINAI], *an old Indian*
WHITE BOY, *eight or ten years old*
FOUR BUFFALO DANCERS
BEAR
EVIL SPIRIT
MEDICINE MAN
THREE IROQUOIS BRAVES
FOUR MEDICINE MAKERS
THREE THUNDERBIRDS
INDIAN MAIDEN
FIVE SIOUX BRAVES

COSTUMES

STORYTELLER: *Bright-colored blanket. Colored headdress with one feather. A long pipe in his hand.*
WHITE BOY: *Usual clothing.*
BUFFALO DANCERS: *Typical Indian suits. Grotesque masks, with horns attached. Masks may be made from paper sacks.*

BEAR: *Fur coat and cap and a mask.*

EVIL SPIRIT: *Long black robe, a mask, and a pointed cap.*

MEDICINE MAN: *Headdress of bright beads and feathers. Indian suit brightly decorated and trimmed with feathers.*

IROQUOIS BRAVES: *Typical Indian suits. Headdresses with only a few feathers.*

MEDICINE MAKERS: *Masks to represent the bear, the fox, and other animals of the woods. Plain coats.*

THUNDERBIRDS: *Black suits, with white streaks representing lightning. Streaks are sewn to the suits.*

INDIAN MAIDEN: *Wig of black hair with long braids. Wig may be made of black stockings. Fringed blouse and skirt of tan cambric trimmed with beads and embroidery.*

SIOUX BRAVES: *Typical Indian suits. Elaborate feather headdresses.*

SCENE: *Out of doors. The stage is decorated with branches and autumn berries. A small Indian wigwam may be placed at the back of the stage if space is available.*

When curtain rises, the STORYTELLER *is seated on the floor near right front corner of stage. The* WHITE BOY *is seated on a low box near him.*

PART I: UNIVERSAL INDIAN LEGENDS

WHITE BOY. You like your pipe very much, don't you, Okinai?

STORYTELLER. Heap much, little white boy. Indians all like pipes because they are gifts of Great Spirit.

WHITE BOY. Then I know there must be an interesting story about the first pipe. Won't you please tell it to me?

STORYTELLER. White boys like stories too much, but Okinai likes to tell.

WHITE BOY. Will you tell me the legend of the pipe?

STORYTELLER. Many, many moons ago the red men of the land had been quarreling with one another. The Great Spirit did not wish his children to quarrel as white men do so he called them to a great rocky mountain. He waved his hand toward the mountain and it turned into a huge mound of soft red clay. He took some of the clay into his hand and fashioned there the first peace pipe. The others made pipes like that of the Great Spirit, and since that time nearly every Indian has made a pilgrimage to this mountain and made there a peace pipe just as the Great Spirit did.

WHITE BOY. That is a fine story, but where did the tobacco to be used in these pipes come from?

STORYTELLER. That is an older story than the one I have just told you. Once long ago when the good spirits

still lived on earth, one of these spirits lay down by a
bonfire and went to sleep. An enemy of his passed and
rolled the spirit so near the fire that the sparks fell on
his hair. The spirit was so frightened when he awoke
and found his hair on fire that he ran across the prairie.
Wherever bits of his burned hair fell, a tobacco plant
grew. Ever since that time the Indians have known
and used tobacco in their pipes of peace.

WHITE BOY. I had never heard that story. [*Pauses.*] Now
I wish I could see one of the Indian dances.

STORYTELLER. I will call a few of the braves before the
wigwam and they will dance the buffalo dance for you.
In this they entreat the Great Spirit to send buffaloes
from all directions. They ask protection from the
bears and wild animals that might interfere with their
hunt and they drive away the evil spirit of famine from
the camp.

[*The music of the Indian dance is heard as the*
FOUR BUFFALO DANCERS *enter in single file. They
have their arms folded and lean slightly forward as they
move with high steps around the stage. Any suitable
Indian music may be used for the buffalo dance, the
movements of which follow.*]

MOVEMENT 1. *After circling the stage once, one*
DANCER *stands at each corner of stage. He holds his*

left hand across his chest and motions off stage with his right. [This represents calling in the buffalo from all corners of the earth.] The DANCER turns, faces in the opposite direction, and repeats the motioning.

MOVEMENT 2. ALL *face toward center of circle and dance toward center with high, prancing steps. The left hand is held on the hip and the right is waved high over the head. When they reach center, they turn around to the right and dance back to original places in corners.*

MOVEMENT 3. ALL *turn left and dance around in a circle twice, pause, turn in opposite direction; repeat.*

MOVEMENT 4. ALL *pause in corners and fold arms, standing very straight as* DANCER *from right corner and* DANCER *from left back corner go to center of stage, where they dance around each other and return to their corners.*

MOVEMENT 5. *The other two* DANCERS *repeat the movement above.* ALL *turn to right, fold arms, bend forward, and dance to the left in circle twice around stage.* ALL *face center, dance to center, turn sharply to left, and return to corners.*

MOVEMENT 6. *The* BEAR *now enters and comes growling to the center of stage.* DANCERS *dance about him, gradually coming nearer to him. They extend their arms over him and give quick exclamations.*

MOVEMENT 7. DANCERS *face the* BEAR *and dance backward away from him. They then quickly advance very close to him, back away, and return to original places in circle. From here they throw what appear to be pieces of meat to the* BEAR. *He takes them and runs off stage.* DANCERS *then dance about to the right.*

MOVEMENT 8. *When the* DANCERS *return to their corners,* EVIL SPIRIT *enters slowly and quietly. He comes to the very center of stage, extends hands, and turns slowly around.* DANCERS *give a whoop when they see him, dance threateningly toward him, wave their arms at him, and chase him from the stage.* ALL *follow him off in single file.*

STORYTELLER. That is the buffalo dance. Did you see how the braves beckoned the buffalo from every corner of the earth and how they satisfied the hunger of the bear that might interfere with the hunt? Then Evil Spirit appeared, but he was quickly driven from the camp. It has been an Indian belief that evil spirits bring much trouble and sorrow. In the Indian camps, as you may know, the medicine man drove the evil spirits away. The medicine man is a very interesting Indian character, and will tell you of himself and of his work in the tribe.

[*Enter the* MEDICINE MAN. *Comes near the front of stage.*]

MEDICINE MAN. I am the medicine man of the Indian tribe. When the Indian is sick I drive away the evil spirit that is in him and make him well. The gods tell the medicine man the sacrifice they want when the Indians have offended them. I am skilled in the ways of magic and in the use of the herbs of the woods. [*Exits.*]

WHITE BOY. Were these things known in all the Indian tribes just the same?

STORYTELLER. The things that you have just seen were common to nearly all the Indian tribes of North America. Now I shall show you some scenes from one of the Iroquois stories.

PART II: IROQUOIS LEGEND

Enter THREE IROQUOIS BRAVES. *Two of them are almost carrying the third one, who appears to be badly injured. Near center of stage they pause and set the wounded man on the floor. They come near the front of stage.*

FIRST BRAVE. Why should we be bothered with that wounded Indian? We shall never catch any game if we have to carry him through the woods.

SECOND BRAVE. There is a ditch over there. Shall we throw him in there?

FIRST BRAVE. Yes, he will probably die anyway, and there is no use in carrying him farther.

[FIRST *and* SECOND BRAVE *pick up the* THIRD BRAVE *and place him near side of stage. The two then exit. Enter* MEDICINE MAN. *Goes to the side of* THIRD BRAVE.]

MEDICINE MAN. Here is an Indian who is hurt. I will put some herbs on his wounds and he will soon be better. [*He bends over the* THIRD BRAVE *and pretends to dress his wounds.* THIRD BRAVE *soon is able to stand.*]

THIRD BRAVE. Where are my comrades who were hunting with me?

MEDICINE MAN. They left you here to die when you became a burden to them, but I dressed your wounds and gave you herbs that made you stronger.

THIRD BRAVE. I am grateful to you.

MEDICINE MAN. Before you leave the forest you will have a vision which will well repay you for the pain you have endured so bravely.

[*Exit* MEDICINE MAN. THIRD BRAVE *walks toward back of stage.*]

THIRD BRAVE. That medicine man must be skilled in magic. Only a few minutes ago I was near death and now I am as strong as ever. [*Looks off stage.*] What strange-looking men those are coming near me!

[*Enter* MEDICINE MAKERS. *They dance around the stage. They then form a circle near the side of stage.*]

MEDICINE MAKERS [*solemnly, in unison*]. We are the medicine makers of the woods. We provide the herbs that make you well. Without us the medicine man could not do his work. We are the medicine makers of the woods. [*Exit.*]

THIRD BRAVE. I have seen a great sight; few humans have ever beheld the medicine makers of the woods.

[*Enter* THUNDERBIRDS, *who dance around* THIRD BRAVE *while someone off stage beats on drums to represent thunder.*]

FIRST THUNDERBIRD. We are the thunderbirds. We will take you home.

THUNDERBIRDS. Shut your eyes and we will take you to your home in a clash of thunder.

[THUNDERBIRDS *run around* THIRD BRAVE *two or three times and, with a loud clash made by drums and cymbals off stage, exit, taking* THIRD BRAVE *with them.*]

STORYTELLER. And the Thunderbirds did take the Indian brave home—or so the legend goes. And there a lovely Indian maiden was waiting for him.

[*Enter* INDIAN MAIDEN; THIRD BRAVE *returns to stage.*]

INDIAN MAIDEN. I knew you would return home. The braves who accompanied you said you were dead, but a dream told me it was not so.

THIRD BRAVE. They were false friends, but the things

I saw in the woods well repaid me for the trouble those braves caused me.

[*Exit* INDIAN MAIDEN *and* BRAVE, *hand in hand.*]

STORYTELLER. I have time for just one more story. This is from the Sioux Indians.

PART III: SIOUX LEGEND

Enter the FIVE SIOUX BRAVES.

FIRST BRAVE. The hand of the maiden I want to win is worthy of great labor, but the things she asks me to do are very hard indeed.

SECOND BRAVE. Tell us what those things are. You have befriended us along the way here and we shall repay you in any way we can.

FIRST BRAVE. I fear you will not be able to help me.

SECOND BRAVE. But we will be able to help you, for we [*indicating* THIRD, FOURTH, *and* FIFTH BRAVES *and self*] are good spirits, walking the earth disguised as human braves.

FIRST BRAVE. How thankful I am; for near the home of the maiden I love there is a stone so great that it keeps away all the sunshine. She demands that I roll it away.

THIRD BRAVE. That I can easily do. I am Strong Arm, and I can move mountains at my will. I will go at once and do as she asks. [*Exits hurriedly.*]

FIRST BRAVE. I had no idea that was the great Strong

Arm. The stone will be as nothing before him. There is yet another task before me that I cannot perform. A great lake has crept very near the home of the maiden's tribe. They fear it will cover the houses and wigwams. She bids me drink away the waters of the lake, but that I cannot do.

SECOND BRAVE. That I can easily do. I am known as Thirsty One, and if I chose, I could drink the ocean away during the night. I shall be glad to drink the lake for I am thirsty. [*Exits.*]

FIRST BRAVE. I have heard of the spirit called Thirsty One, but I never thought I should see him. Perhaps someone will help me perform the other tasks and then the Indian maiden shall become my wife. The third task is to foretell for her when the warriors are returning from the hunt a full day before they arrive.

FOURTH BRAVE. I shall serve you there when the time comes, for I am Sharp Ear, and I can even hear things growing. The thing you are to do will be easy for me.

FIRST BRAVE. Then I have just one more task to do. I must run a race with the maiden and beat her, but I fear I cannot do that for she runs as swiftly as the wind.

FIFTH BRAVE. I will make myself look just like you, and I shall run the race with the maiden.

FIRST BRAVE. But do you believe you can outrun one so swift as she is?

FIFTH BRAVE. I am called Swift One. No one can run faster than I, for I am the one who gives speed to those who run. I can easily run in your place, and no one can beat me against my will.

FIRST BRAVE. Then the lovely maiden shall be mine, and I owe it all to these friends whom I did not know were spirits, but whom I aided as I would aid anyone in need. Come, we shall do the remaining things she asks and I shall be given her hand.

[*Exit* FIRST BRAVE, FOURTH BRAVE, *and* FIFTH BRAVE.]

STORYTELLER. These are only a few snatches from the wealth of legends that belong to every Indian tribe. Some of the legends are much the same in all the tribes, and others vary greatly. But, white boy, you must go to bed now, so old Indian says good night.

CURTAIN

THE DAY BEFORE THANKSGIVING

Time of Playing: *About fifteen minutes*

CHARACTERS

Mother
Abigail, *ten years old*
James, *twelve years old*
John, *eight years old*
Squanto ⎫
Samoset ⎭ *friendly Indians*
Father

COSTUMES

Mother: *Dark-colored dress made with long, full skirt and white collar.*

Abigail: *Dress made similar to the one described above, but of a little brighter color.*

James, John, *and* Father: *Black coats, knee trousers, buckles on shoes, etc.*

Squanto *and* Samoset: *Typical Indian dress.*

Time: *November, 1621.*

Scene: *The interior of a log cabin at Plymouth, Massachusetts. The cabin is furnished simply. There are a table, a cupboard, several chairs, and a couple of benches, on one of which are a bucket and a wash basin. A few rag rugs or some animal skins may be scattered about. On the hearth is a kettle, and on the mantel are candlesticks. Near by is a wood basket.*

As the curtain rises, MOTHER *is seen mixing some dough at the table, on which are some cooking utensils, a pan of beans, and other materials.* ABIGAIL *is watching her,* JAMES *is fixing the fire, and* JOHN *is standing at the window.*

MOTHER. Children, if I'm to get the bread baked and the beans looked over before your father comes with the turkeys, you'll all have to help me.

ABIGAIL. Please let me help with the bread, Mother. I know how to mix it.

MOTHER. Very well, Abigail.

[ABIGAIL *begins mixing the dough.*]

JAMES. John and I can look over the beans for the feast.

MOTHER. That will help a lot, but first you'd better fetch some water and some wood.

JAMES [*picking up the wood basket*]. Oh, all right. [*Exits.*]

JOHN [*grumbling as he gets the water bucket and follows* JAMES]. I just wish Father hadn't gone to shoot turkeys!

ABIGAIL. Wasn't it fine that Governor Bradford ordered all of the people of Plymouth to cel-celebrate? I'm so happy!

MOTHER [*reprovingly*]. You should be thankful instead of happy, for that is what the day is for. It's to give thanks to our Heavenly Father for the homes he has given us in this new land, for our abundant harvests, and for the peace that is ours.

ABIGAIL [*putting bread into fireplace to bake*]. Yes, I know, but can't I feel thankful and kind of happy, too, because we're to cel-celebrate, and have a big dinner?

JOHN [*entering with bucket*]. I don't want no celebration!

MOTHER. Hush, John! You don't know anything about one. We've never yet had a Thanksgiving.

JOHN. I don't care! I don't want any Thanksgiving!

MOTHER [*surprised*]. Why, John!

JAMES [*entering with wood*]. He's angry because the old deacon tapped him with his stick last Sunday.

MOTHER [*amazed*]. What? Did one of my children go to sleep during services?

JOHN. I wasn't asleep! I was just thinking, when that mean old deacon hit me! Just wait till I'm big and—and I'll—

MOTHER. That will do, John! Sit over there [*indicating a chair*], and think what you'll tell your father when he comes home.

[JOHN *sits in chair.*]

ABIGAIL. I'm glad Governor Bradford asked the Indians to our cel-celebration.

JAMES. Massasoit and ninety of his braves are coming.

JOHN. I don't like Indians. All they say is "ugh."

ABIGAIL. You like Squanto and Samoset. They're Indians.

JOHN. Well, Squanto talks like we do, and Samoset can say "Welcome, Englishmen," and a lot more.

ABIGAIL. Squanto taught us how to plant corn and—

JAMES [*breaking in*]. And how to hunt. Father learned how to shoot turkeys from him.

MOTHER. We have a great many things to thank the Indians for. We'd have starved last winter if they hadn't brought us food.

JOHN. Samoset and Squanto are all right, but I don't like Massasoit! If I were Captain Miles Standish, I'd fight him, I would!

JAMES. But Massasoit is Samoset's chief. You remember that he made a treaty with us, don't you?

JOHN. I don't care if he did, and I don't want any Thanksgiving!

MOTHER. James and Abigail, you'd better help me and leave John alone for awhile.

JAMES. He's still angry because that mean old — I mean the deacon tapped him with his rod. [*Takes pan of beans from table.*]

JOHN. I wasn't sleeping! I was just thinking, and he hit me!

MOTHER. That will do, son.

[*A shuffling of feet is heard outside the door, followed by a thud. Latch is raised.* JAMES *opens door.*]

JAMES [*opening door*]. Squanto and Samoset! Come in!

MOTHER [*as* SQUANTO *and* SAMOSET *enter*]. Welcome, friends.

SAMOSET. Welcome, Englishmen!

[ABIGAIL *laughs, then puts hand over mouth.*]

SQUANTO. We brought a deer—meat for Thanksgiving.

MOTHER [*surprised*]. A deer? Then we can have sweet venison for tomorrow. Thank you, thank you.

ABIGAIL [*jumping about gleefully*]. Isn't it wonderful? I'm so happy!

JAMES [*to* SQUANTO *and* SAMOSET]. We'll have lots of meat, won't we, Squanto? Won't we, Samoset? Father went to shoot some turkeys.

MOTHER [*to the Indians*]. Sit down and rest. [*They seat themselves.*] We'll eat when Father comes.

SQUANTO [*motioning to* JOHN, *who sits with head lowered*]. Is John sick?

MOTHER. Go and speak to your friends, John.

JOHN [*taking a stand between* SQUANTO *and* SAMOSET]. How do you do? [*Puts an arm around each.*]

SQUANTO. You're a good boy, John.

JOHN. No, I've been bad. I got—angry. [*Hangs head.*]

SQUANTO. Too bad. You tell Squanto what make you angry?

JOHN. If you'll tell me a story, I will.

SQUANTO [*laughs;* SAMOSET *joins in*]. What you want me to tell you?

JOHN. What you did when you were small like me, and how you learned to talk English.

SQUANTO. When I was small, I lived like all the boys of my tribe, and like most of the other Indian boys. We fished in the streams and lakes. We planted corn and hunted. And in the fall we gathered fruit and nuts. One day a big ship came.

JOHN. Like the "Mayflower"?

SQUANTO. Bigger. Much bigger. I wanted to see it, so I went close. Some men caught me and carried me away. We sailed for weeks and weeks. I learned that they were Spaniards. They took me to their country. I worked there for several years as a slave. Then I went to the British Isles. There I learned to speak English. Later I came back home on a ship, but I couldn't find my tribe.

JOHN. Did they move away?

SQUANTO. I think they must have died—or been killed.

JOHN. What did you do then?

SQUANTO. I met Samoset and he took me to his chief, Massasoit. And now here I am in Plymouth.

JOHN. I want to make a big garden. Will you show me how to plant corn?

SQUANTO. Yes.

SAMOSET. Samoset catch fish to plant with corn. Grow big ears!

JOHN. Goody! I'll have a big garden.

ABIGAIL. May I help?

JOHN. Yes, and so may you, James. Then we can raise a lot of corn for another Thanksgiving!

MOTHER [*surprised*]. Another Thanksgiving, John?

JOHN [*sheepishly*]. Yes, Mother. [*Pauses.*] That's what I was thinking about when—the deacon—hit me with his stick.

SQUANTO. Did he hit you? [*Rises.*] I'll hit him.

SAMOSET [*also rising*]. Me hit.

JOHN [*speaking rapidly and shoving* SQUANTO *and* SAMOSET *toward their chairs*]. No, no, Samoset! No, no, Squanto! You mustn't. You mustn't. He thought that I was asleep, and we shouldn't sleep in church.

JAMES. It looked as if you were asleep.

JOHN. He hit me when I wasn't, and it made me mad, so I didn't want *any* Thanksgiving.

SQUANTO [*laughs*]. Big man hits little boy because he wants another Thanksgiving. [SAMOSET *laughs.*] But you are not angry now?

JOHN. Oh, no!

SQUANTO. That what you want to tell Squanto?

JOHN. Y—yes, and about making a garden. Wouldn't it be nice to have a Thanksgiving celebration every year? I was going to ask Governor Bradford about it, after the service, when—the deacon—hit me.

MOTHER. Son, why didn't you tell me about all this?

JOHN. Because I was angry. [*Quickly smiling.*] But I'm not angry now!

MOTHER. You must control that temper.

JOHN [*contritely*]. Yes, Mother.

SQUANTO [*laying hand on* JOHN's *head*]. John is a good boy and I will help him make a good garden.

SAMOSET. Samoset help John.

ABIGAIL. Wouldn't it be wonderful to have a Thanksgiving every year as John wants to do?

MOTHER. It would be something to work for all the year.

[A *stamping of feet is heard without. The door is flung open. Enter* FATHER, *with a gun and a huge pack.*]

CHILDREN. Father, Father! What did you get? Let me see. [*They crowd around him, hanging on him, and helping him.*]

FATHER. One at a time; one at a time! [*Catches sight of* SQUANTO *and* SAMOSET.] Welcome, friends, welcome!

SQUANTO *and* SAMOSET. Welcome, welcome!

FATHER. Good thing you Indians taught me how to shoot turkeys. See that? [*Indicating pack.*] Got enough birds to last for a week of Thanksgiving.

JOHN. We have a deer, too.

FATHER. A deer?

MOTHER. Our friends brought it to us.

[MOTHER *and* ABIGAIL *put supper on the table.*]

FATHER. That's splendid. What a Thanksgiving we'll have!

ABIGAIL. Father, John is going to ask Governor Bradford if we can't have a Thanksgiving every year.

FATHER [*thoughtfully*]. Every year? A celebration for the harvest? Wonderful! [*Gives* JAMES *gun. Slips off coat. Washes hands.*]

MOTHER. Surely God has been good to us in this new land.

FATHER. I think we can all say amen to that.

MOTHER. Supper's ready. Move up the chairs. [*To* SAMOSET *and* SQUANTO.] Won't you eat with us?

SQUANTO. No, thank you. Supper will be waiting for us. We must go.

[SAMOSET *and* SQUANTO *go to the door.* CHILDREN *move chairs around the table; family stand at places. The family bow their heads.* SAMOSET *and* SQUANTO *watch, then bow theirs.*]

FATHER. Dear Heavenly Father, we thank Thee for all the blessings that Thou hast bestowed upon us. We thank Thee for our homes, for our abundant crops, for the good friends Thou hast sent us, and for the peace that is ours. Amen.

ALL. Amen. [*Raise heads as curtain falls.*]

CURTAIN

MR. CRABIT CELEBRATES THANKSGIVING

TIME OF PLAYING: *About fifteen minutes*

CHARACTERS

MR. CRABIT, *a cross old gentleman*
MARY, *his ten-year-old niece*
JIMMY, *his twelve-year-old nephew*
HELEN, *a neighbor girl*
FREDDIE, *a neighbor boy*
TURKEY
PUMPKIN
SPIRIT OF THANKSGIVINGS PAST

COSTUMES

MR. CRABIT: *Ordinary adult clothing.*

MARY, JIMMY, HELEN, *and* FREDDIE: *Ordinary children's apparel.*

TURKEY: *Wears a turkey mask, or wears a large picture of a turkey pinned on suit.*

PUMPKIN: *Wears an orange crepe-paper pumpkin over head. Green streamers hang from top of head.*

SPIRIT OF THANKSGIVINGS PAST: *White dress, trimmed with colored streamers.*

SCENE: *Living room in the Crabit home. Furniture as desired. At the rise of the curtain, MARY, JIMMY,*

51

HELEN, *and* FREDDIE *are seated about the room. They appear very sad.*

HELEN. I can't understand why anyone wouldn't want to celebrate Thanksgiving when he has plenty of money. We always had a big time until Daddy was hurt.

FREDDIE. Mother feels terrible because we can't have a big Thanksgiving dinner this year, but she says we just can't afford it. Maybe things will be better for us later on and then we can have a big celebration.

JIMMY. Uncle Crabit has plenty of money to celebrate in just the finest possible way, but when I asked him about it he said, "Rubbish, there is no sense to it all. It's just another day, and besides I have nothing to be thankful for."

MARY. Isn't that just terrible? Jimmy and I asked him if he couldn't celebrate it this year just on our account. We get awfully lonesome living in this big house with him alone, but he wouldn't change his mind about Thanksgiving for anything.

HELEN. He is a horrid, mean person.

MARY. Oh, don't say that. He really was very kind to give us a home here with him and he really isn't a mean man. He just seems to lack the Thanksgiving spirit.

FREDDIE. Maybe if we would talk to him he would change his mind. Helen and I hate to have just a small Thanksgiving celebration, but it seems worse when you just aren't going to have any at all.

JIMMY. Here comes Uncle now. I just know he won't change his mind, no matter what you say to him.

[*Enter* MR. CRABIT, *looking ill-tempered.*]

MARY [*rising*]. Come here and meet my girl friend, Uncle. This is Helen Smith, who lives on the corner.

[HELEN *rises.*]

JIMMY [*rising*]. And this is her brother Freddie.

MR. CRABIT [*gruffly*]. Oh! Hello. Awful weather we have. I never saw such weather. How do they expect a person to live in such weather, I'd like to know.

FREDDIE. It isn't bad weather for Thanksgiving time, though, Mr. Crabit. By the way, how are you planning to celebrate?

MR. CRABIT. I'm not planning on celebrating Thanksgiving at all. It's stuff and nonsense filling yourself up with turkey when all it does for you is give you the gout. There's no sense to it all.

HELEN. Oh, but surely on Mary and Jimmy's account you are going to have a Thanksgiving dinner. They would feel terrible if you didn't.

MR. CRABIT. Then it is time they got over such nonsense. Clear out of here now, you young ones. I want to read.

[*Exit* CHILDREN *sadly, while* MR. CRABIT *settles himself*

in an easy chair and picks up the paper to read.] Thanks-
giving, humph! There isn't a thing to it. Not a thing.
[*Reads a moment and then drops off to sleep. Enter*
TURKEY. *Comes close to* MR. CRABIT'S *chair.*]

TURKEY. Gobble! Gobble! Gobble! So you don't believe in Thanksgiving, do you, old Mr. Crabit? Well,
you have changed your tune since you were a boy, for
then Thanksgiving was a big occasion in your life.

MR. CRABIT [*awakening and turning to the* TURKEY].
Who are you?

TURKEY. I am the spirit of the turkey that you had for a
Thanksgiving dinner long ago. Don't you remember
me? I was a fine big gobbler but when you went to
catch me I turned around and bit your leg, just like
this. [*Pinches* MR. CRABIT'S *leg.*]

MR. CRABIT [*screaming with pain*]. Stop! Stop, I tell you!
I remember you very well. How my leg did hurt, but I
got even with you after all, for my father came, and together we cut off your head. Then Mother roasted you
with chestnut dressing. What a meal that was!

TURKEY. You didn't think that Thanksgiving was nonsense then, did you?

MR. CRABIT. Times have changed since then. People
aren't what they used to be.

TURKEY. No, they are older and crankier, but children and
Thanksgiving are the same. Remember that! [*Exits.*]

MR. CRABIT. I must be getting childish. Whatever made me remember that old turkey and the time I had with it? I'll forget it. Where is the market page of this paper? That is more important than Thanksgiving.

[*Enter* PUMPKIN, *who comes near the chair.*]

PUMPKIN. Oh, no, it isn't, Mr. Crabit. The market page is never as important as Thanksgiving, and I remember the time when you didn't think so either.

MR. CRABIT. Now who are you that comes to pester me?

PUMPKIN. I am the pumpkin that helped make the pie that you ate one Thanksgiving long ago. Don't you remember? You ate a big piece for dinner, and after dinner your Uncle Henry gave you his piece; then in the afternoon you went into the pantry and ate another large helping. You have forgotten me, maybe, but I know a way of reminding you of myself. I will give you a little touch of the stomach-ache you had that night so long ago. [*Goes over to* MR. CRABIT *and holds his hands over him.*]

MR. CRABIT [*screaming with pain*]. Stop! You are killing me! I don't need any reminder of that stomach-ache. I shall never forget it as long as I live.

PUMPKIN. Still, when it was over, you said that Thanksgiving was worth it all, anyway.

MR. CRABIT. So I did. Well, I must have been a little

fool, for that stomach-ache was bad, I tell you.   Still that was a big day.   I remember that Thanksgiving just as plainly as if it were yesterday.

PUMPKIN.   I thought you would if I jarred your memory a little.   Well, I must be going.   There are a few more old cranks I have to visit this night to wake up their recollections, too.   Happy Thanksgiving to you and your niece and nephew! [*Exits, running.*]

MR. CRABIT.   Maybe it is selfish of me not to have a Thanksgiving dinner for the children.   Still they probably don't care as much about it as they pretend.

[*Enter* SPIRIT OF THANKSGIVINGS PAST *who comes to* MR. CRABIT'S *side.*]

SPIRIT.   Oh, no, they won't, Mr. Crabit.   They will remember it just as you have remembered those happy days of your childhood, for they were happy days, weren't they, even if they did have their little pains?   They will remember this sad Thanksgiving of theirs and the crabby old uncle who didn't have time to spend one day of the year in making them happy.   Children remember such things better than you think, and it is a dreadful thing to lose the love of a child, especially when it is one of your own family.

MR. CRABIT.   Who are you, talking to me like this, and what do you know about children and their memories?

SPIRIT. I know everything about them for I am the spirit of the Thanksgivings that have come and gone. Since 1621 I have seen children and grownups observe this day, and I know that for every loyal American it is a time of rightful rejoicing. That is why I dislike seeing Mary and Jimmy robbed of their glad day. When you were a lad, your mother worked very hard and in the face of many difficulties to make the day a glad one for you. Don't you remember?

MR. CRABIT [*standing*]. Yes, I do remember well, and I am ashamed of myself for the way I have acted with my own sister's children. It isn't that I don't like them and want them to be happy, but I have been so used to just thinking of myself that I was selfish with them. I am thankful that it is not too late yet. [*Calling.*] Children! Children!

[*The* SPIRIT *leaves as* MARY *and* JIMMY *come running in.* HELEN *and* FREDDIE *are with them.*]

JIMMY. What is it, Uncle?

MARY. Is there something wrong, Uncle?

MR. CRABIT. Yes, there is something wrong and *I* am the something. I have been a pigheaded, selfish, stingy, thoughtless old fool. Just because I was too old to have the fun I used to have at Thanksgiving, I thought it was foolishness, but now I have come to my senses.

MARY. Why, Uncle, whatever has come over you?

MR. CRABIT. We are going to have the finest Thanksgiving dinner that you ever saw and have it right here. These friends of yours are invited. Go out and ask in, oh, say about twenty others. I am sure you can find that many children in the whole town who are not planning on having a real Thanksgiving dinner at home.

JIMMY. Do you really mean it, Uncle? I always said you were a jolly good fellow if you would just take time to think it over.

HELEN. Come, Mary, let me help you plan it. What a happy time it will be!

MARY. How can we ever thank you, Uncle?

MR. CRABIT. Don't thank me. Thank the—oh, well, just let the thanks go. [*Aside.*] They would think I was crazy if I told them of my visitors. [*To* MARY *and* JIMMY.] Hurry now and make your plans. We will have a genuine old-time Thanksgiving Day.

[*Exit* CHILDREN, *laughing and chatting.*]

CURTAIN

THANKSGIVING IN MOTHER GOOSE LAND

TIME OF PLAYING: *About fifteen minutes*

CHARACTERS

MOTHER GOOSE	MARJORIE DAW
FLEETFOOT } *messengers*	JACK
HASTY JACK	JILL
TOM, *the piper's son*	MARY, *who had a little lamb*
MOTHER HUBBARD	TOMMY TUCKER
QUEEN OF HEARTS	MISS MUFFET
KNAVE OF HEARTS	BOPEEP
JACK-BE-NIMBLE	MISTRESS MARY
POLLY	BOY BLUE
KING COLE	HUMPTY DUMPTY
TRAIN BEARER	JACK HORNER
THREE FIDDLERS	OLD WOMAN WHO LIVED IN
PIPE BEARER	A SHOE
BOWL BEARER	CHILDREN OF OLD WOMAN,
SIMPLE SIMON	*any number*

COSTUMES

All Mother Goose characters wear traditional Mother Goose costumes. FLEETFOOT *and* HASTY JACK *wear tennis shoes and gym suits.*

SCENE: *Living room in the home of* MOTHER GOOSE. *Door at one side. Window at opposite side. Table at center. A cupboard at one side. Curtain rises upon* MOTHER GOOSE *giving instructions to* FLEETFOOT *and* HASTY JACK.

MOTHER GOOSE. You, Fleetfoot, and you, Hasty Jack, as my messengers, are the first ones whom I shall tell of my latest and best plan!

FLEETFOOT. Dear Mother Goose, what is your plan?

HASTY JACK. And what can we do?

MOTHER GOOSE. One question at a time, please. I am going to give a Thanksgiving party. This year has been a very prosperous one in our land, and I want you to call my people together for a celebration. So you, Fleetfoot, go to the south and west, inviting all as you go, and Hasty Jack, you go to the north and east to see that no one is left out.

FLEETFOOT *and* HASTY JACK. We shall do our best.

[*Exit* FLEETFOOT *and* HASTY JACK.]

MOTHER GOOSE. I must begin preparing at once. [*As she talks, places several dishes of food on the table.*] What shall I do? What shall I do to get ready? Perhaps some of my guests will bring something. If Simple Simon would only bring that pieman and if Tom, the piper's son, would bring his pig, it would help so much with the dinner. What a wonderful roast that pig would make! [*Glances out window.*] Oh, here comes Tom now!

[*Enter* Tom *carrying a roaster.*]

Tom. I stole a pig and got it roasted. It's ready to be eaten.

Mother Goose. Your pig is already roasted? [*Takes roaster and places it on table.*] How that will help!

[*Enter* Hasty Jack *and* Fleetfoot, *out of breath.*]

Hasty Jack. The people of Mother Goose Land are delighted. Everyone is coming. Who would have thought of having such a party but you, Mother Goose?

Fleetfoot. Why, Tom is here already. [*Peeks in roaster.*] And what is this? A roasted pig? What a fine party we are going to have!

[*Enter* Mother Hubbard, *leaning on cane.*]

Mother Hubbard. Oh, Mother Goose, I went to my cupboard to find something to bring to the party, but there was not even a bone for my dog Snyder.

Mother Goose. Do not worry, Mother Hubbard. You are very welcome at our party, and we hope you shall find more than a bone here.

Fleetfoot [*sniffing*]. I smell tarts! Mother Goose, have you been baking tarts for our party?

Mother Goose. You must be mistaken.

Tom [*stepping to window*]. The Queen and Knave of Hearts are coming. Perhaps they've brought some tarts.

[*Enter* Queen *and* Knave of Hearts. Knave *is carrying a tray of tarts.*]

QUEEN OF HEARTS. That wicked Knave stole my tarts, but I have forced him to bring them to the party.

KNAVE [*giving tarts to* MOTHER GOOSE]. Here they are, dear Mother Goose!

[MOTHER GOOSE *places tarts on table. Enter* JACK-BE-NIMBLE, *hopping.*]

ALL.

> Jack be nimble;
> Jack be quick!

JACK-BE-NIMBLE [*places candle on floor and jumps over it*].
> Jack jump over the candlestick.

[*Enter* POLLY *with teakettle.*]

MOTHER GOOSE.

> Polly, put the kettle on;
> Polly, put the kettle on,
> And we'll all have tea.

POLLY. I've already put my kettle on. [*Places teakettle on table.*] The tea is ready.

[*Loud knocking outside.*]

ALL. Who can that be?

[MOTHER GOOSE *opens door. Enter* OLD KING COLE, TRAIN BEARER, PIPE BEARER, BOWL BEARER, *and* THREE FIDDLERS. ALL *sing* "Old King Cole." *As pipe and bowl are mentioned in song,* BEARERS *lift up these articles.* THE THREE FIDDLERS *pretend to fiddle as they are mentioned. Enter* SIMPLE SIMON.]

KING [*scornfully*]. Bah! To think that Simple Simon should follow me!

SIMPLE SIMON [*lisping*].

> Simple Simon met a pieman
> Going to the fair.
> Said Simple Simon to the pieman,
> "Let me taste your ware."
> Said the pieman to Simple Simon,
> "Show me first your penny."
> Said Simple Simon to the pieman,
> "Indeed I haven't any."

[*Enter* MARJORIE DAW. ALL *sing* "Marjorie Daw." *Enter* JACK *and* JILL *with a pail of water.*]

JACK. We fell down with our first pail of water, but we went back for another. Here it is.

MOTHER GOOSE [*taking pail*]. Thank you, children. But, dear me, I'm afraid you took quite a tumble.

JILL. No, we're all right. When we came rolling down the hill, we passed Mary with her lamb. She will be here soon.

[*Enter* MARY *pulling a toy lamb.*]

MARY. Here is my lamb. I started without her, but she followed me. I'm afraid that a lamb is not worthy of the society of a king and queen and all the other people of Mother Goose Land.

MOTHER GOOSE. We are very glad that the lamb has come, for you would not seem like Mary if you did not have your lamb.

[*Enter* TOMMY TUCKER.]

MOTHER GOOSE. Welcome to our party, Tommy Tucker.

POLLY. Are you ready to sing for your supper?

MOTHER GOOSE. No, this is to be a real party for Tommy. He need not sing for his supper, and we hope he may find more than bread and butter. Tommy, with all these fair ladies in Mother Goose Land, I don't see why you say "How shall I marry without any wife?"

TOMMY TUCKER. Perhaps I will surprise you one of these days, Mother Goose.

[*Enter* MISS MUFFET, *running.*]

MISS MUFFET. Oh, I was so frightened! I was sitting on my tuffet eating my breakfast of curds and whey when along came a spider—

ALL.

And sat down beside her,
And frightened Miss Muffet away.

MISS MUFFET. How did you know?

MARJORIE DAW. You're an old friend, Miss Muffet. We always know your trouble.

MOTHER GOOSE. We are glad that spider came along to-day for it brought you just in time for our party.

[*Enter* BOPEEP. ALL *sing* "Little Bopeep." *Enter* MISTRESS MARY, *carrying flowers.*]

ALL.

Mistress Mary, quite contrary,
How does your garden grow?

MISTRESS MARY.

With silver bells and cockleshells,
And pretty maids all in a row.

Here are some of the flowers from my garden. I brought them for the party.

MOTHER GOOSE [*taking the flowers*]. Thank you, dear Mary. [*Puts flowers in a vase.*]

[*Sound of horn outside.*]

BOPEEP. That must be Boy Blue.

MOTHER GOOSE [*going to door and calling*].

Little Boy Blue,
Come blow your horn;
The sheep's in the meadow,
The cow's in the corn.

[*Enter* BOY BLUE.]

BOY BLUE. And for once I'm not under a haystack fast asleep. I'm always awake for the good parties in Mother Goose Land.

[*Enter* HUMPTY DUMPTY.]

MOTHER GOOSE. Are you here safely, Humpty?

HUMPTY DUMPTY. Yes, very safely. I came very slowly so that nothing would happen to me on the way to the party. You must pardon my being a trifle late.

[*Enter* JACK HORNER.]

JACK HORNER. Hello, everybody.

ALL. Hello, Jack.

JACK HORNER. Aren't you surprised to see me here?

MOTHER GOOSE. Yes, rather.

JACK HORNER. Well, I thought I'd come over and try a piece of Thanksgiving pie for a change. Say, Mother Goose, did you put in a plum for me?

MOTHER GOOSE. No, Jack Horner, I never thought of it. Now, let me see! Yes, everyone is here. Suppose each one of us tells of something for which he is thankful.

JACK-BE-NIMBLE. Sure, I'll be first. I'm thankful for my candlestick and lots of room to jump over it. [*Jumps over candlestick.*]

TOMMY TUCKER. I'm thankful for my supper, only I want it *quick.*

TOM [*looking around*]. Oh! Where is the Old Woman Who Lives in a Shoe?

MOTHER GOOSE. Hasty Jack, didn't you invite *her* and all her children?

HASTY JACK. Oh—Mother Goose, I forgot all about her.

Will you forgive me? What shall I do? What shall I do?

MOTHER GOOSE. Go for her at once. You go, too, Fleet-foot. Hurry!

MOTHER HUBBARD. How terrible! Those children probably haven't as much to eat as my dog Snyder, and he hasn't even a bone. Oh me, oh my! What are we coming to?

KING COLE. Imagine having all those children here! Why don't they stay in their shoe? They will step on my train. [WOMAN WHO LIVES IN A SHOE *and* CHILDREN *enter.*] Ugh!

MOTHER GOOSE. Welcome to our Thanksgiving party!

WOMAN WHO LIVES IN A SHOE [*shaking hands with* MOTHER GOOSE]. How thankful I am that you have invited my family to this wonderful party, Mother Goose! Our shoe is so small and our family so large that it would have been hard for us to celebrate Thanksgiving at home.

TOMMY TUCKER. To show Mother Goose how thankful we are for her thoughtfulness, let's all sing [*names a Thanksgiving song*].

[ALL *sing the song suggested by* TOMMY TUCKER.]

CURTAIN

NOVEMBER VISITORS

TIME OF PLAYING: *About fifteen minutes*

CHARACTERS

THREE GIRLS
ROBERT LOUIS STEVENSON
PIRATES, *three or more*
CYRUS FIELD
JOHN PHILIP SOUSA
LOUISA MAY ALCOTT
MEG
JO
BETH } *characters in "Little Women"*
AMY

COSTUMES

GIRLS: *Usual clothing.*

ROBERT LOUIS STEVENSON: *Dark, long-haired wig. Old-fashioned suit [of the style worn toward the end of the nineteenth century].*

PIRATES: *Typical pirate costumes.*

CYRUS FIELD: *Old-fashioned black suit and hat [of the style worn during the Civil War period].*

JOHN PHILIP SOUSA: *Military band uniform.*

LOUISA MAY ALCOTT: *Dress made with long, full skirt [Civil War period].*

MEG, JO, BETH, *and* AMY: *Dresses made with long, full skirts* [*Civil War period*].

SCENE: *The* THREE GIRLS *are seated around a table when the curtain rises. Books and papers are on the table.*

FIRST GIRL. I have often heard that November is a dreary month, but I don't think it is. It seems to me to be a very fine month.

SECOND GIRL. Book Week comes in November. That is always a happy time, for at school and in the library new books are placed on the shelves for us to read.

THIRD GIRL. Everyone loves Book Week, for then we have a chance to get acquainted with many new friends that lie between the covers of the new books we read.

SECOND GIRL. Thanksgiving belongs to November, too. That is an honor no month would overlook.

FIRST GIRL. No doubt there are many other interesting events in November, too.

[*Enter* ROBERT LOUIS STEVENSON.]

STEVENSON. You are right, my children. I am Robert Louis Stevenson, and my birthday comes in the month of November. You probably know me best from my poems in the "Child's Garden of Verses." Would you like to hear some of my poems?

GIRLS. Oh, we should like that very much!

STEVENSON. Very well, then. [*Recites several of his well-known poems.*] A great many children have read and enjoyed my book, "Treasure Island." Boys like to pretend they are pirates and act just as the characters in my book did.

FIRST GIRL. And boys aren't the only ones who like to read about your pirates!

[PIRATES *enter and sing the pirate song found in the book,* "Treasure Island."]

STEVENSON. I must be going. There are many other interesting characters in November, so I must not take up all the time. Good-by.

GIRLS. Good-by, Robert Louis Stevenson. Come again.

[*Enter* CYRUS FIELD.]

FIELD. Good afternoon, children. Since you seem to be entertaining people who have birthdays in November, I thought I would stop in and see you for a little while.

FIRST GIRL. I am sure we are glad to see you, but I don't believe we know who you are.

FIELD. I know you don't recognize me, for my picture is not usually seen in the papers at this time of the year as is that of honorable Mr. Turkey. I am Cyrus Field, the man who promoted the laying of the Atlantic cable, so that messages could be sent from our country to

Europe and news from there could be hurried back to us.

SECOND GIRL. I remember reading about you in our history book. You had a great deal of trouble before you finally were able to send messages by cable, didn't you, Mr. Field?

FIELD. Yes, we had several misfortunes, but by never giving up we were finally successful.

THIRD GIRL. Tell us about it, Mr. Field.

FIELD. In 1857 my friends and I began the great task of laying the cable from America to Ireland. This was the same year that the first telegraph wire was stretched across the United States. We started out from Ireland with miles and miles of copper wire, but were doomed to disappointment. Four hundred miles out the wire broke, and we had to return defeated. Twice we failed, and the world laughed at us for trying to do such a thing as to lay a cable across the ocean. At last, in 1858, a cable was successfully stretched across the Atlantic. Queen Victoria of England and President Buchanan of the United States exchanged greetings by its aid and we rejoiced in our victory. But after three months the messages became fainter and fainter and finally could not be heard at all. We had to try again. The Civil War delayed our efforts for the time, but in 1865 we were really successful.

SECOND GIRL. You did well to keep at a task that looked so impossible. You deserve a place of honor on the November calendar.

FIELD. Now I must say good-by, for I'm sure you'll have more November visitors. [*Exits.*]

GIRLS. Good-by, Mr. Field.

[*Enter* SOUSA *carrying a baton.*]

FIRST GIRL. Oh, I know who you are. You are John Philip Sousa, the famous band leader.

SOUSA. Yes, I am John Philip Sousa, and I claim November for my birthday month. Would you like to hear some of my music?

GIRLS. Yes, we would.

SOUSA. Then I will have my band play. [*Goes to door, as if band is off stage. Selection is played on the phonograph.* "The Stars and Stripes Forever" *would be suitable.* SOUSA *waves his baton as if directing the band.*]

SECOND GIRL. Tell us something about yourself before you play another number for us, Mr. Sousa.

SOUSA. I was born in 1854, in Washington, D. C. I always had a great love for music and especially for stirring marches. I believe that it is good for a person to hear good music. I was leader of the Marine Band from 1880 to 1892. After that the band I directed became known under my own name. Would you like to hear another of my marches?

GIRLS. Yes, indeed!

[*While another selection is played,* SOUSA *waves his baton as if directing the band. Exit* SOUSA *when music ends.*]

FIRST GIRL. I wonder if we will have any more visitors.

[*Enter* LOUISA MAY ALCOTT; *curtsies.*]

THIRD GIRL. Here is someone now. My, it is an old-fashioned girl!

LOUISA ALCOTT. Yes, I am an old-fashioned girl, and I have written many stories about the girls and boys of my time. I am Louisa May Alcott, the author of "Little Women," "Little Men," "Under the Lilacs," and many other tales.

SECOND GIRL. Oh, I have always wanted to meet you. I know your story of "Little Women" almost by heart.

[MEG, JO, BETH, *and* AMY *enter and dramatize a section of* "Little Women."]

FIRST GIRL. You have made us very happy by coming here, Miss Alcott. I wish you could stay with us longer.

LOUISA ALCOTT. I would like to, for you modern children are quite different from those I wrote about back in the Civil War period; but I must be on my way. There are other groups of children to be reminded of some of the well-known people who celebrate their birthdays in

November. Good-by, girls. [*Exits, followed by* MEG, JO, BETH, *and* AMY.]

GIRLS. Good-by.

FIRST GIRL. What an eventful time this has been! I am sure this is one November we shall never forget.

SECOND GIRL. You are right. Hurrah for November!

THIRD GIRL. Hurrah for November!

CURTAIN

THE PRESIDENT'S PROCLAMATION

CHARACTERS

JEAN   MARY   HELEN

COSTUMES

Characters wear their usual clothing. No special costumes needed.

SCENE: *A living room.* JEAN, MARY, *and* HELEN *are seated about the room.* MARY *has a newspaper, while* JEAN *and* HELEN *have books.*

JEAN. What are you reading, Mary?

MARY. Something that is very, very important at this time of year.

HELEN. Then it must be about Thanksgiving.

MARY. You are right, Helen. How did you ever guess it?

JEAN. That is all I have heard or thought about for a week. What does the daily paper have to say about Thanksgiving?

MARY. It has the President's Thanksgiving proclamation printed here today. You know, every year the President issues a special statement setting aside a day in November for Thanksgiving Day. In his message he usually calls our attention to some of the things for which we can be thankful. Shall I read it for you?

HELEN. Wait. Let us start at the beginning. I have just
been reading the first Thanksgiving Day proclamation
ever issued by a President of the United States. It was
written by George Washington in 1789. Shall I read it?
MARY *and* JEAN. Yes, do.
HELEN [*stands and reads distinctly the* "First Thanksgiving
Proclamation," *by George Washington, 1789.*]

"Now, therefore, I do recommend and assign Thursday,
the 26th day of November next, to be devoted by the
people of these states to the service of that great and glori-
ous Being, who is the beneficent author of all the good
that was, that is, or that will be. That we may then all unite
in rendering unto Him our sincere and humble thanks
for His kind care and protection of the people of this country previous to their becoming a nation—for the single
and manifold mercies, and for the favorable interpellation
of His providence, in the course and conclusion of the late
war."

JEAN. How splendid! I can almost see the dignified
Father of His Country appearing before the officials
of the day and reading that proclamation.
MARY. Yes, and you may be sure that many a merry
Thanksgiving dinner followed that order, for the people
of those days enjoyed this holiday as much as we do.
JEAN. I have found another proclamation that I believe

you will want to hear. It is the one of Theodore Roosevelt in 1905. The country had changed much since the days of Washington, but the spirit of Thanksgiving was always the same.

HELEN. Read the proclamation for us.

JEAN [*stands and reads distinctly the* "Thanksgiving Day Proclamation," *by Theodore Roosevelt, 1905.*]

"When, nearly three centuries ago, the first settlers came to the country which has now become this great republic, they fronted not only hardship and privation but terrible risk to their lives. In those grim years the custom grew of setting apart one day in each year for a special service of thanksgiving to the Almighty for preserving the people through the changing seasons. The custom has now become national and hallowed by immemorial usage. We live in easier and more plentiful times than our forefathers, the men who with rugged strength faced the rugged days; and yet the dangers to our national life are quite as great now as at any time in our history. It is eminently fitting that once a year our people should set apart a day for praise and thanksgiving to the Giver of good, and, at the same time that they express their thankfulness for the abundant mercies received, should manfully acknowledge their shortcomings and pledge themselves solemnly and in good faith to strive to overcome them. During the past year we have been blessed with plentiful crops. Our business prosperity has been great. No other people has ever stood on as high a level of material well-being as ours now stands. We are not threatened by foes from without. The foes from whom we should pray to be delivered are our own passions, appetites, and follies; and against these there is always need that we should war.

Therefore, I now set apart Thursday, the thirtieth day of this November, as a day of thanksgiving for the past and of prayer for the future; and on that day I ask that throughout the land the people gather in their homes and places of worship, and in rendering thanks unto the Most High for the manifold blessings of the past year, consecrate themselves to a lifetime of cleanliness, honor and wisdom, so that this nation may do its allotted work on the earth in a manner worthy of those who founded it and of those who preserved it."

HELEN. That, too, is a splendid proclamation; but wait, and we shall bring this ceremony up to date. Mary, read the President's Proclamation for 19—.

[MARY *stands and reads the proclamation for the year.*]

MARY. And so Thanksgiving is always the same great holiday in this country that gave it birth!

CURTAIN

THE TWO THANKSGIVINGS

Time of Playing: *About twenty minutes*

CHARACTERS

Pasipika [*leader*], *the Indian chief*
Ieska [*interpreter*], *his white wife*
Princess Ehawee [*laughing maid*], *their sick daughter*
Ikicaga [*to grow to be something*], *their son*
Wicaka [*faithful*], *the son's playmate, a girl*
Luta [*to stick to*], *an Indian maiden*
Waditaka [*brave*], *the chief's friend*
Waasniyan [*healer*], *the medicine man*
Wahdokeca [*artist*]
Mahkahwee [*earth maiden*]
Okihi [*boy*]   } *a group of young*
Akaga [*boy*]   *Indians*
Pashuta [*girl*]
Dorothy, *a college friend of* Wicaka
Ned, *a college friend of* Ikicaga

COSTUMES

In Scenes I *and* II *all characters wear Indian clothing.*
In Scene III *ordinary clothing is worn.*

Scene I: The Old Thanksgiving

Time: *The night before Thanksgiving.*

79

SCENE: *A part of an Indian village showing the camp of* PASIPIKA, *the Indian chief. A wigwam is on one side of the stage; a mock campfire on the other. The following characters are grouped about the campfire:* PASIPIKA, IESKA, PRINCESS EHAWEE, IKICAGA, WICAKA, LUTA, *and* WADITAKA.

IESKA. Ehawee, my laughing maid, what ails you? You laugh no longer. The color has flown from your cheeks. For days you have eaten so little. Ieska, your mother, grows afraid for you.

EHAWEE. It is nothing, Mama Ieska, only that always I am so tired, so tired. Of late my body has been feeling strange pains, strange sharp pains—sometimes only dull ache. But today the pain is so sharp I am afraid I might forget I am a chieftain's daughter, and scream with all my strength.

PASIPIKA. Brave little daughter. Go into the wigwam and lie down. Scream, if it will ease your pain. I would do anything if I might bear your pain for you. Your brother Ikicaga will go at once for the medicine man.

[*Exit* IKICAGA. EHAWEE *starts for the wigwam.*]

EHAWEE [*pausing by the flap of the wigwam*]. The songs of the streams and the birds are so beautiful. I wonder, Mama Ieska, if I shall ever hear them and see the flowers again. [*Enters wigwam.*]

IESKA. If only there were something we could do. My little one feels the shadow upon her already. I will go sing to her. [*Goes to wigwam and soon afterwards starts singing or humming an Indian lullaby within the wigwam. The others may stop and listen.*]

[*Enter* IKICAGA *with* WAASNIYAN]

PASIPIKA. Pause for awhile, Waasniyan, our loyal medicine man. Ieska is singing to her little laughing maid who laughs no more.

WAASNIYAN. If there be a full moon, oh Chief, I will try my new healing potion for your bird. I have burned the powder from the root of the Ni-ho tree, danced the dance to frighten evil spirits from your door, and worn my most ferocious mask over my face until I am weary. If this fails tonight, there is nothing more I can do.

LUTA. Some powerful spirit is fighting for her soul. I can feel it in the air.

WADITAKA. Everyone loves Princess Ehawee. I am sure it is no hatred in *our* village that has brought this evil upon her.

PASIPIKA. No, not in this village. But there is another village near—the camp of the white men. They are tonight having a big powwow to celebrate what they call Thanksgiving Day.

WAASNIYAN. Why did we not think of it sooner? There must be some evil person in that camp who has cast a spell over our Ehawee. I go to her at once. [*Goes to wigwam.*]

PASIPIKA. Can they never leave us alone?

WADITAKA. They have driven us from the land that was ours.

LUTA. They have killed or driven away the buffalo that used to graze on the plains in large numbers.

IKICAGA. They have used their strange shooting rods on the wild turkeys so much that now we must hunt all day for even a sight of game.

WICAKA. But they have shown us better ways to grow grain in the good earth.

PASIPIKA. Wicaka, long have you been the favorite playmate for my son. Too often do you defend the ways of the white men. Take care that someday they do not cast a spell on you, too.

[WAASNIYAN *and* IESKA *come from the wigwam, the latter weeping.*]

WAASNIYAN. Ehawee, the laughing maid, will never laugh again. To the happy hunting ground she has gone. There will she hear the song of the stream, and the birds. She is in the arms of the Great Spirit.

IESKA. I am filled with grief. Never will I forget her suffering. Ehawee, my little one. Ehawee, my brave one.

PASIPIKA. And I am filled with revenge. These white men talking of friendship and thanksgiving. Bah!

WADITAKA. We might seek revenge, oh Pasipika.

PASIPIKA. How?

WADITAKA. How did we before? Steal upon them while they are sleeping. Burn their village. Kill their braves. Steal their papooses. Scalp their squaws. [*Arises.*] Shall I beat the tom-tom?

WAASNIYAN. Wait, Chief Pasipika. I beg of you to think before you strike. No longer are we the strongest tribe. Our brave warriors are dead or white haired. Our young braves are too young for a successful war now. We have but bows and arrows. They are too weak against the rods that make loud noises and spit fire.

IESKA. Pasipika, I, too, beg you to forget revenge in this hour of my grief. The Great Spirit giveth and taketh. Death is natural; revenge is stupid. They would only conquer again, and push us from our homes. Ehawee is laughing again on the Ever-Summer Plains and would frown at blood shed for her.

PASIPIKA. Ieska is right. Let the tom-tom rest. While we are left, we few, we will cling to the ways of our race—Indians forever, while we last.

[ALL *sing some mournful Indian song as the curtain falls.*]

Scene II

Time: *Thanksgiving night.*

Scene: *Same as* Scene I. *About the campfire are the following:* Ikicaga, Luta, Wicaka, Wahdokeca, Mahkahwee, Okihi, Akaga, *and* Pashuta.

Ikicaga. I have called you together, my young friends, for counsel. The council fire burns low. I will speak at once of the problems. What says my father of our future?

Wahdokeca. Chief Pasipika says that while we are left, we few, we will cling to the customs of our race.

Mahkahwee. Indians forever, while we last.

Wicaka. Ikicaga has other plans for us.

Okihi. Other plans?

Akaga. What does he mean?

Pashuta. Tell us, Ikicaga.

Ikicaga. The white men have strange ways. They have learned new ways. They eat and are not always hungry. They are warm. They sleep, even in the long winter nights. They do not die from sickness as we do.

Luta. And what of all that, Ikicaga?

Wicaka. Can you not see? We can learn of them.

Okihi. You would have us forsake our fathers?

Pashuta. You would have us live as do the white men?

Wahdokeca: He has been affected by the moon.

AKAGA. And he, the Chief's own son.

LUTA. Luta is my name. It means "to stick to." I shall stick to the ways of my fathers. Once an Indian, always an Indian.

WAHDOKECA. Luta is right. Can you change your red skin, crazy Ikicaga?

MAHKAHWEE. It is late. I leave such foolishness to seek sleep. I am not white, but I, too, must sleep. Ha, ha!

PASHUTA. We will not tell your father, Ikicaga, if you will say no more. [*Exit* ALL, *laughing, except* LUTA, WICAKA, *and* IKICAGA.]

LUTA. Your father would be very angry with you for this night.

IKICAGA. I cannot believe they thought me crazy.

WICAKA. I, Wicaka, believe in your dream. My name means faithful, and I will be faithful to you, Ikicaga. Shall we not go, alone?

IKICAGA. Yes, unless Luta will change her mind.

LUTA. No, never. Go, if you will. Go to the white men and see what they will do to you. Your thoughts will shrivel when they make you suffer. [*Exits.*]

IKICAGA. We two will have our adventures. We will learn the ways of the white men and come back and teach our people.

WICAKA. First, let us put aside all hatred so we may go to them with open minds.

IKICAGA. It is well. Give me your hand.

[WICAKA *and* IKICAGA *join hands.*]

WICAKA. We go to learn the ways of the white men with open minds and hearts, knowing no hatred.

IKICAGA. We go with friendship so we may return with knowledge to help our people. Be it so and guide us, Great Spirit.

[*Soft music, as curtain falls.*]

SCENE III: THE NEW THANKSGIVING

TIME: *The day before Thanksgiving eight years later.*

SCENE: WICAKA's *room at college. Her friend* DOROTHY *is watching her pack her clothes for departure.*

DOROTHY. It will be lonesome here without you, Wicaka. I wish you weren't going.

WICAKA. But I must go, Dorothy.

[*Knock is heard at door.*]

IKICAGA. May I come in?

WICAKA. Oh, here is Ikicaga now. Yes, come in.

[*Enter* IKICAGA *and* NED.]

IKICAGA. Aren't you ready, Wicaka? I'm afraid you girls have been doing more chatting than packing.

DOROTHY. I just said I didn't want her to go, and she said she had to.

[ALL *laugh.*]

IKICAGA. Certainly she has to.

NED. There's something strange about you two today. What is it? Where are you going on this day before Thanksgiving?

WICAKA. Back to our home—reservation it is called now.

DOROTHY. But you are no longer an Indian. Here you have graduated from college. You can't mean to bury yourself and all you have learned back on some dirty Indian reservation.

NED. Dorothy! Shame on you to speak of their home that way. But why do you go, Ikicaga? You have a wonderful chance to be a great doctor in the hospital here.

IKICAGA. I have a great chance to be a doctor there, too, Ned. Eight years ago we left our people on a Thanksgiving night. What was our reason?

WICAKA. To learn the ways of the white men so that we could go help our people. You couldn't understand.

DOROTHY. We'll try, if you'll tell us more.

IKICAGA. My mother's name was Ieska, which means interpreter. She was stolen from a white man's camp when a young girl.

WICAKA. She married Ikicaga's father, the young chief of the tribe, when the older chief died. She was always curious about the ways of white people because she, herself, is white.

NED. And you two were also eager to see how we lived?

IKICAGA. That's right. I remember about the death of my sister shortly before we left. I am sure now that she had appendicitis. At that time my people believed a curse from the white men killed her. Often our people died from a strange sickness that the medicine man with all his magic couldn't cure. So, I studied to be a doctor.

DOROTHY [*to* WICAKA]. And you, Wicaka, the faithful, became a nurse so you could help him.

NED. Tell me, have we been very cruel to you?

IKICAGA. No, Ned, though we were pretty frightened at first. But this is the happiest Thanksgiving of my life. We are both so thankful for all of the things we have learned—and for our new friends.

WICAKA. Now we must hurry and put to work what we have learned in these years. Come, Ikicaga. Good-by, dear friends.

DOROTHY. Good-by, Wicaka. Don't forget us.

IKICAGA. When you come to see us, I'll have the medicine man dance for you, and wear his ugly mask.

[*Exit* WICAKA *and* IKICAGA]

NED. They really have something to be thankful for. I have too. I'm thankful that I had a chance to know two real Americans like that.

CURTAIN

CHILDREN OF PLYMOUTH

TIME OF PLAYING: *About thirty minutes*

CHARACTERS

READER

MARY
VIRGINIA } *Pilgrim girls*
HOPE

BILL
FRANK
DAVID } *Pilgrim boys*
JAMES
JOHN

LITTLE WOLF, *Indian boy*
MERIWATER, *Indian girl*

COSTUMES

READER: *Usual clothing.*

PILGRIM GIRLS: *Typical Pilgrim dresses, made with long full skirts and white collars.* [HOPE *wears a dark-colored dressing gown in* SCENE I.]

PILGRIM BOYS: *Typical Pilgrim costumes: short trousers, long hose, buckles on shoes, etc.*

LITTLE WOLF *and* MERIWATER: *Usual Indian dress.*

LITTLE WOLF *carries a bag with a salt fish in it.*
MERIWATER *carries a bag of shelled corn.*

PROLOGUE

Before the Curtain

READER.

Come with me, my friends,
And let us delve into the files of history.
Let us go back to the seventeenth century,
To that first season the Pilgrims spent in their new land.
We find them battling with that gray wolf, Winter;
Find them huddled together for warmth,
Many ill, many starving, many dying.

And often from the forest's edge
Came the gruesome threat of the redskin
As his hunting party went by,
Wanting to attack, yet fearing
The strength of the white man.
Had the Indians but known the facts,
Plymouth would have gone the way
Of many of the colonies before it;
Followed the path, perchance,
Of those founded by Raleigh and Gilbert—
Lost on the great American shore
And no traces left of their people.

SCENE I

TIME: *Late winter, 1621.*

SCENE: *Door at right. Fireplace at back center. Rifle above fireplace. Chair at each side of fireplace, facing center. At left of stage, a lounge. Small table with a candle on it at right.*

At the rise of the curtain HOPE *is lying on the lounge.* VIRGINIA *is seated at the left of the fireplace.* MARY *is walking toward the door.*

MARY [*looking out the door*]. Spring! [*Pauses, then turns.*] It is coming, girls. Aren't you glad? Old Man Winter will soon be making his last stand. In a few weeks the buds will be out and beginning to swell. Oh, what a dreadful time we have had! [*Goes back to seat, face in hands.*] Poor Mother! Poor Daddy! [*Sobs.*] They gave their lives in search of freedom, and in the service of the God they loved.

VIRGINIA [*sadly*]. Only a few mothers left! My mother is gone, too, God bless her. Every family has lost some member. Some families are completely gone. [*Pauses.*] Oh, if only we could have landed in Virginia, where the climate is not so severe, perhaps our loved ones would be here today.

HOPE. I am so weak I can hardly move. [*Gets up slowly.*] Will it ever end? First Father, then Mother went to their reward. Girls, nearly all of the older people are gone. [*In distress.*] Oh, if we had only stayed in Holland!

MARY. Day by day that colony [*points*] on yonder hill has grown, until it is larger than the colony of the living down here in the valley. Yesterday someone saw an Indian looking down at us from the hills.

VIRGINIA. Yes, there is a wicked tribe back in the forest which would attack if it thought it dared. If that tribe only knew just how defenseless we really are—

HOPE [*breaking in*]. But they can't find out! The village of the dead is hidden by growing wheat. [*In fright.*] Oh, but what if they should attack and kill us all!

MARY [*springs up, wringing hands*]. Don't, Hope! Don't even think of such a thing! If we have to go through much more of this terrible fear, sickness, and hunger— [*Pauses, hysterical.*] Oh, I wish I were with my father and mother!

VIRGINIA [*goes to comfort* MARY; *puts arm around her*]. Come, Mary, you can't give up like that; none of us can. Our parents wouldn't want us to do such a thing. [*Gives her handkerchief.*] Here now, dry your eyes and smile. [MARY *does so.*] That is much better. [VIRGINIA *goes back to seat.*]

MARY. I am sorry, girls. Will you forgive me? [*Pauses.*] Yes, they would want us to carry on.

[*Enter* BILL, *all out of breath.*]

BILL. What do you suppose has happened now?

MARY, VIRGINIA, *and* HOPE. What?

BILL. A bundle of arrows, tied with a rattlesnake skin, has just been delivered to our sick governor [MARY, VIRGINIA, *and* HOPE *draw around* BILL] by a huge Indian brave.

HOPE [*slowly and softly*]. That means—

MARY [*almost in hysterics*]. Oh, no! We can't have that!

VIRGINIA [*angrily*]. They don't dare attack. They are too cowardly.

BILL. Don't worry, Virginia. We all told Miles Standish we would fight. If they must have war, let them come.

[*Enter* FRANK *and* DAVID, *laughing.*]

FRANK. Such a frightened Indian no one will ever see again. Did you see how he held it, David?

[*The rest look at these two.*]

DAVID. Whoever said that an Indian never shows emotion has never seen that brave. Evidently he has met Miles Standish before.

FRANK [*as the rest try to learn what they are talking about*]. Bill, you left too soon. You should have seen the answer Miles Standish sent to their war message.

VIRGINIA. Tell us, boys! What has happened? We were so frightened!

FRANK. It is a rather long story, but I'll try to shorten it. Governor Carver called Miles Standish and told him to answer the Indian warrior's message. Miles Standish took the rattlesnake skin, dumped out the arrows, and refilled it with powder and bullets.

DAVID [*cutting in*]. And when he handed it to the Indian, the poor fellow was so frightened that he almost dropped it. We need have no more fear of those Indians.

CURTAIN

INTERLUDE

Before the Curtain

READER.

And then at last came the springtime,
And with it new courage for the Pilgrims.
Many were the hardships they had suffered;
But now, as a blessing from heaven,
Came that gentle breeze from the south.
And the Pilgrims strolled forth to the cornfields.
Busy were they with their new plantings,
And soon forgotten were their cares and their troubles—
Perhaps not forgotten
But pushed back into the pigeonholes of memory,
Not to be brought out again
Until some day in the distant future.

Scene II

TIME: *Spring, 1621.*

SCENE: *Same as* SCENE I. *At the rise of the curtain* HOPE *is lying on the lounge. No one else is in the room. She sits up.*

HOPE. Carry on. [*Puts hand to forehead.*] God wants us to carry on. [*Pauses.*] I'm so glad spring has come. Yes, everyone seems happier now. [*Pauses.*] I, too, shall soon be well. Poor John Carver! He gave his life, too. He was the last of the ill to go. And Governor Bradford has already taken his place. [*Pauses.*] Every soul in this colony has but one ambition and that is to carry on. [*Excitedly.*] We are going to succeed now. [*Rises.*] Nothing can stop us!

[*Enter* JAMES *and* JOHN *in good spirits.*]

JAMES. Look, John, the patient is up. Hurrah! Why, Hope, we thought you were ill.

HOPE [*smiles*]. Does one have to stay ill forever?

JAMES. Look at those rosy cheeks, those sparkling eyes.

JOHN [*in mock confusion*]. Oh, I say, James, are you playing doctor, or lover? I am a little confused. [*Smiles.*]

[*Enter* FRANK *and* DAVID *in high spirits.*]

FRANK. There is no need to argue. I saw a sign, I did.

DAVID. So did I! So did I! This may be America, but the signs are the same the whole world over.

JOHN [*emphatically*]. Will you gentlemen be so kind as to tell us what you are discussing?

DAVLD [*almost shouting*]. Spring, my child! Spring! Wild geese and ducks have been going up the coast all day. That is a sign that never fails. [*Pauses.*] Another sign! I saw a group of strange singing birds in the forest.

FRANK. And that can mean only one thing. Mother Nature has stepped in to save us!

CURTAIN

SCENE III

TIME: *One month later.*

SCENE: *Same as* SCENE II. *Flowers on the table and around the fireplace.* MARY *is sweeping the floor at center of stage.* VIRGINIA *is churning at left.* HOPE *is at right, sewing.*

MARY. To sweep, or not to sweep. [*Pause.*] That is the question. [*Sweeps hard.*] Oh [*leaning on broom*], it would be better to steal off into the woods and pass the time of day with those two little Indians, Little Wolf and Meriwater, and discuss the many things they understand which no white man understands—how the deer makes his living; where the gray squirrel stores his food; all the secrets of the wild life; the ways of the little animals of the forest—[*Sweeps listlessly.*]

HOPE [*as she sews*]. To sew, or not to sew. [*Pauses.*] That's the question. Yes! Why couldn't we have been Indian children? They don't have to sew. [*Thinks.*] Well, on second thought they do sew, but they use bone needles and rawhide thread. What fun it would be to sew with such tools!

VIRGINIA [*as she churns*]. To churn, or not to churn. That is the question. [*Churns slowly.*] If I don't churn, I will be churned. If I do churn [*pauses*], what do I get? Come, girls, guess.

HOPE. Who gives it to you?

VIRGINIA. Did I say ask questions, or guess?

MARY. You get to go boating on the river!

HOPE. No, no, not that! [*Pauses.*] You get to pick flowers in the meadow.

VIRGINIA. Such guessers! Now, girls, what could anyone get, who churned? Butter, friends, butter!

HOPE [*laughing and pointing to* VIRGINIA]. She gets butter!

MARY [*to* HOPE]. A fatty substance found in cream, a product of milk.

HOPE [*hand at ear*]. Hear ye! Someone approaches our domicile!

[*Enter* FRANK, BILL, JOHN, DAVID, *and* JAMES *with sleeves rolled up. They carry hoes over their shoulders. They form a circle around the stage.*]

Boys [*singing to tune of* "Auld Lang Syne" *as they enter*].

    Oh, winter now is far away;
    And this we're glad to say,
    For corn must be planted in the ground,
    And the cattle must have hay.

CHORUS

    [*Rubbing hands together.*]
    For blisters on our hands we have
[*Leaning forward and rubbing their backs.*]
    And soreness in our backs.
    But when it's winter we'll have food
        [*Pointing to* GIRLS.]
    And you can count on that.

MARY [*going over to couch and putting hand to ear*]. Hark! Hark! Someone is singing!

HOPE [*to* VIRGINIA]. 'Tis true! Did you hear, Virginia?

VIRGINIA. 'Twas but the voices of the elves who make the butter gather.

FRANK. Now, now, my dear Virginia, we are not elves.

BILL [*with a meaningful glance at* FRANK]. Did you say "dear"? [*To* GIRLS.] Nor do we make the butter rise.

JOHN. But we are humans—

FRANK. And we dislike very much having beautiful young ladies make fun of us.

DAVID. What we want to know is, have you girls seen two little Indians named Meriwater and Little Wolf?

MARY. Why?

DAVID. 'Tis but to do and die—'Tis not to reason why!

FRANK [*breaking in; speaks to* DAVID]. A nice quotation, David, but we haven't time. [*Bows to* GIRLS.] Meriwater and Little Wolf, young ladies, were to come and show us how to plant corn properly.

HOPE. When?

JAMES. Today! Now!

VIRGINIA. But where is the corn?

JAMES. They have that, too. [*Looks out.*] Here they are now.

[*Enter* LITTLE WOLF *and* MERIWATER.]

LITTLE WOLF [*extending arm up and forward*]. How!

BOYS *and* GIRLS. Good morning, friends.

JOHN. So glad you came. We have been anxiously waiting for you.

MERIWATER [*goes to* JOHN]. Here is corn. [*Gives* JOHN *sack of corn.*]

JOHN. Thanks, Meriwater. Now, Little Wolf, tell us how to plant it.

MERIWATER [*shakes head*]. Him not know. Indian boy no work; only hunt. [*Points to self.*] Me tell how. [*Takes* BILL's *hoe and pretends to dig.*] Make hole in ground like this. [*Gets corn from sack.*] Take corn.

[*Holds up three fingers.*] This many. Put in place.
[*Reaches in* Little Wolf's *sack and pulls out fish.*
White Boys *and* Girls *hold noses.*] Place 'um with
corn. [*Measures with arms.*] Grow heap big ears!

CURTAIN

Interlude

Before the Curtain

Reader.

And on through the springtime and long summer days
They toiled in their fields and gardens,
Fished in the streams and the sea,
And rebuilt their barns and their dwellings;
Looked on with great satisfaction
As the corn the Indians had helped to plant,
Stretched ever and ever upward,
Till in the sky its tassels seem to be hanging.

And now came the autumn,
The end of the season of growing,
End of their worries and cares,
For a great harvest stood
In their fields and their gardens.
Game was plentiful in the woods;
And the Indians remained ever friendly,
Bringing in tanned skins to trade

With the Pilgrims, for homespun and trinkets;
Wishing the white man well
And much pleased with the way he had treated them.

"Gather around me, my flock;
I have a message of importance to give you."
Thus spoke the great William Bradford,
Governor of the Colony of Plymouth.
"Great our troubles have been;
But now, our worries and sorrows are forgotten.
From the fields, the meadows, the gardens,
The Lord has granted us a bountiful harvest.
Let us set aside this week of autumn
For feasting, and giving thanks to our Saviour.
For, if He had not watched over us
We, too, would certainly have perished.
Go ye, and prepare a feast; you men, to the forest,
And bring back the turkey and the red deer.
Captain Standish, you and your army
Go swiftly to the camp of the red men
And ask them to join us tomorrow,
For, in the eyes of the Lord, they, too, are our brothers."

Scene IV

Time: *Day before Thanksgiving, 1621.*

Scene: *Same as* Scene II, *except for autumn decora-*

tions. DAVID *is seated on lounge.* JOHN *is at the right of the stage, cleaning his gun.*

DAVID. When we landed [*rising and going to look out window*] it was in the dead of winter, cold and death-dealing. Then came the gentle spring, the time of planting; then summer, the time for growing; and now autumn, with its beautiful colors, and large, yellow moon in the nighttime, the harvest moon. Yes, the same old yellow moon we loved to see back in England and Holland. [*Returns to seat.*]

JOHN. Yes, the harvest moon, and, thank the Heavenly Father, we have a great harvest stored away. No more hunger for us! Yes, I am glad winter is on the way, aren't you? Just think of the fun we shall have in the snow and on the ice.

DAVID. Won't it be grand! [*Pauses.*] Do you suppose the Indians will come in to the feast Governor Bradford has ordered? All of the men left for the forest at daybreak this morning. I hope they bring back one of those splendid young turkeys we saw feeding there a few weeks ago.

JOHN. If they don't [*looking over his gun*], I am going to go out myself; I know where a large flock roosts.

[*Enter* FRANK, BILL, *and* JAMES, *each of them carrying an ax.*]

BILL. Hear ye! Hear ye! My gentle young men.

JAMES. There is to be a feast tomorrow; did you know?

FRANK. And a message was delivered to us, saying that if five little boys living in the Colony of Plymouth, Province of Massachusetts, Continent of North America, wanted to eat and eat and eat on the morrow, and days to follow, they must take themselves at once to the woods, and bring back to the settlement many, many armloads of wood for the feast fires.

BILL. So, Johnny, lay down your weapons and come with me.

JAMES. And David, you will need that bed more tomorrow, after the feast.

[*Exit* BOYS. *Enter* MARY, VIRGINIA, *and* HOPE *in good spirits.*]

MARY. I am so glad Governor Bradford called this feast!

HOPE. I am glad, too. As we all know, we have so much for which to be thankful. [ALL *seat themselves.*] Everyone is happy, all of the granaries are full, the cellars are stuffed with vegetables, the forests are loaded with game, and everyone is in good health.

VIRGINIA. Yes, it is quite different from a year ago today, isn't it? We were out in the middle of the cold Atlantic then. Our little ship was leaking, and none of us knew whether we should ever see land again. [*Pauses.*] But now, after all our hardships, we can see many peaceful years ahead for us.

MARY [*goes to door*]. Come, girls! Look! The Indians are coming!

[ALL *rush to door.*]

HOPE. Look at the deer they are carrying. And see the squaws! What do you suppose that is that they are carrying?

VIRGINIA. I don't know, but no doubt it will be good to eat tomorrow.

MARY. The braves have on their war paint. [*Shivers.*] Ugh! Why did they put it on?

HOPE. And they are carrying their bows and arrows. Do you suppose they are going to surprise us?

[ALL *stroll away from door.*]

MARY [*emphatically*]. Of course not; the Indians are our friends.

[*Enter* BILL, *out of breath.*]

BILL. Hello, Virginia! [*To the rest.*] Oh, hello, girls. Er-uh-that is, a certain young lady, who is interested in a certain young man by the name of John Alden, would like very much to have you girls help dress turkeys.

HOPE [*as* GIRLS *rise*]. We shall be delighted. Where is she?

BILL. Down by the meat house. She must have at least twenty turkeys.

MARY. Twenty! Come on, girls! That is five for each one of us.

[ALL *go out, but as* VIRGINIA *starts through door* BILL *calls to her.* MARY *and* HOPE *go on.*]

BILL [*bashfully*]. Oh, I uh—say, Virginia.

VIRGINIA [*stopping*]. Yes?

BILL. I was thinking that—uh—[*stands on one foot, then on the other*] could—uh, would—uh, that is—er—uh—[*scratches opposite leg with toe*] it is a nice fall day, isn't it.

VIRGINIA. Why, yes, Bill; but what is the matter with you?

BILL. Nothing, only—uh—um, you know, Virginia, I sort of like [*pauses*] this beautiful weather we are having. Don't you?

VIRGINIA. Yes! It is beautiful. [*Starts to go.*]

BILL. Don't go! Don't go! I wanted to tell you that I—uh —sort of like you—

VIRGINIA [*smiles*]. Now please don't start that all over again. [*Runs out.*]

BILL [*snaps fingers*]. Why is it that every time I try to talk to her I seem to swell up around the heart and throat, and my tongue and brain won't work in unison?

CURTAIN

INTERLUDE

Before the Curtain

READER.

And so all to the feast did go,
And the Indian and the white man sat down together;
Learned to understand one another
And promised to be friendly ever after;
Smoked the pipe of peace
And through the smoke drifting from it,
Saw the image of the Saviour
As he poured upon them his blessings.
Thus ends our story of Plymouth,
That memorable home of the Pilgrims.
Thus ended the feast of that day,
That ne'er-to-be-forgotten day
When the Pilgrims gave thanks for the bountiful harvest
Bestowed by the Giver of all good gifts.

SCENE V

TIME: *Thanksgiving evening.*

SCENE: *Same as* SCENE IV. *Candles burning. Stage lights low. Fire in fireplace. A Dutch oven with nuts in it by the fire.* HOPE *is sitting on the chair at the right.* MARY *is sitting on the chair at the left.*

VIRGINIA *is seated on the lounge.* JAMES, BILL, *and* FRANK *are sitting on the floor at the right of the stage.* JOHN *and* DAVID *are lying on their stomachs at the left of the stage.*

MARY. Well, boys and girls, the feast is over, the fun is finished, and winter is upon us. How nice it is to have fresh soft snow on the ground again!

JAMES. If my stomach could speak, it would tell you about a boy who tried to eat everything in sight. Wasn't that pumpkin pie good?

VIRGINIA [*smiling*]. I hear John is a wonderful shot.

BILL. Yes, indeed! The most fun I have had since I left Holland was in watching that little Indian outshoot John with his bow and arrow. Was there something in your eye, John?

JOHN. My foot kept slipping and I couldn't hold steady.

HOPE. Now, John, are you sure?

FRANK. Well, those fellows make their living by their bows and arrows. Why shouldn't they be good shots?

JOHN. Wait until next year. Am I going to practice? Well, I'll be ready for a real contest with that little red man by then. I am going to practice until I can hit a target at one hundred yards.

DAVID [*after pause*]. Thanksgiving! That is what Governor Bradford called this week of feasting and offering of thanks. [*Pauses.*] What have we all to be thankful for? Do you realize fully how many reasons we have to be thankful? Many times during the dreadful winter, everyone threatened to go back to Old England when the "Mayflower" sailed in the spring. But did they go? No! Not a single one. When spring came, each took a new grip upon himself. Warm weather gave us new courage. Freedom is what we came after, and freedom is what we have gained. And now, with food plentiful, houses warm, Indians friendly, we are thankful.

HOPE. Yes, every one of us rode into the valley of the shadow of death. Some stayed, but we came back, and for that we should be thankful. A new country is being settled, and we have the honor of being among the first to come to it.

VIRGINIA. I still have my dear father. Oh, how I love him! Thank God, he, too, was not taken from me.

MARY. I, too, have lost the ones dearest to me. [*Pauses.*] It was their wish to make a home in this wonderful land of freedom, and I am thankful I have been given the honor of carrying out that wish.

JOHN. Yes, the hardest part is over. Next spring more people will come from Old England, and our colony will grow and prosper. How glad I, too, am that I was among the first to come.

FRANK. I, too. History will long remember us. Just think, only one English colony was successful before us; that was Jamestown, in Virginia, settled just fourteen years ago.

BILL. Yes, many have lost their lives trying to gain a foothold on this continent. Even we, but for our faith, might have failed. [*Pauses.*] I wonder what sort of place this will be, say, three hundred years from today. Do you suppose they will still have a Thanksgiving Day? Will they know that, but for the young folks, Plymouth would have failed?

JAMES. Are you trying to get me to think? Well, my stomach is too full, and besides that, it is too hard on my mind. I know something lots nicer than thinking.

ALL. What?

JAMES [*gestures*]. In yonder roaring fire you will find a Dutch oven full of nice, brown, roasted nuts. Pull them out, Hope, and let's end this perfect day of feasting as it should be ended.

ALL. Oh! Roasted nuts!

JOHN. I had forgotten all about them.

FRANK [*handing* VIRGINIA *a nut*]. Here, Virginia.

BILL. Give it to me, Virginia, and I will crack it for you.

VIRGINIA [*giving* BILL *the nut*]. You boys are so kind.

JAMES [*giving* MARY *some cracked nuts*]. Here, Mary, I cracked these especially for you.

MARY. Oh, thank you!

JOHN [*giving* HOPE *some cracked nuts*]. Here, Hope,

with my best regards for a very happy ending to the greatest of all Thanksgivings.

BILL. Are we all happy?

ALL. We most certainly are.

BILL. My greatest regret is—

JOHN [*cutting in*]. What?

BILL. That it is three hundred and sixty-five days until the next Thanksgiving.

[ALL *laugh.*]

CURTAIN

THANKSGIVING BY CHANCE

TIME OF PLAYING: *About forty minutes*

CHARACTERS

GRANDMA JACKSON, *an elderly woman*

RICHARD, *a boy about eleven*

JUNE, *a girl about twelve*

HENRY, *the father, a man resigned to his fate*

LAURA, *the mother, a very scatterbrained person*

JOE, *the delicatessen delivery boy*

COSTUMES

GRANDMA JACKSON: *A neat-looking, rather old-fashioned house dress; pince-nez.*

RICHARD: *School clothing. A jacket and cap in* SCENE I.

JUNE: *School clothing. A coat and a hat or cap in* SCENE I.

HENRY: *Business suit. An overcoat and a hat at the beginning of* SCENE I.

LAURA: *A street suit, a hat, and gloves in* SCENE I; *a colorful house dress in* SCENE II.

JOE: *Sport trousers and slipover sweater.*

SCENE I

TIME: *The day before Thanksgiving.*

SCENE: *A typical middle-class living room-dining room.*

Doors at left and at back center. Desk with tele-phone at right. Chair near desk. Davenport at right center. Hall tree near back center. Table and five chairs at left center. Other furniture as desired.

As the curtain rises the telephone is ringing. GRANDMA *answers.*

GRANDMA. Hello. [*Pauses.*] Yes, this is she speaking. [*Pauses.*] Oh, Eloise, how are you? [*Pauses.*] No, I wasn't busy. I wasn't doing a thing. I'm all alone, and I'm so glad you called. My grandchildren aren't home from school yet. June has orchestra practice tonight and Richard is playing football, but they'll be here soon. [*Pauses.*] Their mother? Oh, Laura's down-town. She ought to be home soon, but you never can tell about Laura. She's up at the Good Neighbor Club meeting. They're canning applesauce for the orphanage this afternoon. [*Pauses.*]

Thanksgiving? Oh, yes, I guess we'll have turkey. Laura spoke about picking up some things for Thanks-giving dinner while she's downtown. [*Pauses.*] My, you are lucky to have your turkey all stuffed. [*Pauses.*] What? Your nephew won a turkey at the Strand Theater! Well, can you beat that!

Say, I may win something myself. Just this afternoon a boy from the Schwartz Delicatessen was around selling chances on a Thanksgiving dinner—all prepared and ready to eat. [*Pauses.*] No, I really don't expect to be lucky. Land sakes! I buy a number on something about every week, and I've never won anything yet. [*Laughs.*] Everybody in the family says I never will. [*Pauses.*]

RICHARD [*outside*]. So long, Jerry! I'll be seeing you Monday. Don't eat too much Thanksgiving dinner! [*Enter* RICHARD *through door at back center.*]

GRANDMA. Here's Richard now. [*Pauses.*] Sure, I'll call you the first of the week. Good-by. [*Hangs up phone.*]

RICHARD [*taking off jacket and cap and throwing them on the davenport*]. Hi, Grandma! Jiminy crickets! [*Looks around.*] Where is everybody? When's supper gonna be ready? Boy, oh boy! Am I hungry!

GRANDMA [*picking up* RICHARD'S *wraps and hanging them on the hall tree*]. It isn't time for your father yet. He has some extra work at the office. But June ought to be home from orchestra practice any time.

RICHARD. Where's Mom *this* time?

GRANDMA. She should be here by now. She went up to the Good Neighbor Club meeting. They're canning applesauce for the orphanage this afternoon.

RICHARD. Well, I want something to eat. Anything in the refrigerator?

GRANDMA. Not much. Your mother said she'd get some things for supper downtown.

Richard. I'll see what there is. [*Exits left.*]

[Grandma *seats herself on the davenport and picks up a magazine. Enter* June, *carrying a violin case.*]

June. Hello, Grandma. [*Puts down violin case and sits by* Grandma.]

Grandma. Hello, dear. How was orchestra practice?

June [*taking off coat and hat*]. Oh, we practiced the music we're going to play at the Christmas program. And guess what! Miss Walker says that if I keep practicing my piece, "Dancing Snowflakes," I can play it at the mid-term graduation next month.

Grandma. Why, that's fine, June! We'll all be so proud of you.

June. How's the Thanksgiving dinner coming, Grandma? Is the turkey all ready?

Grandma. Not yet, June. Your mother said she'd get one downtown.

June. I do hope she doesn't forget!

[*Enter* Richard.]

Richard. Boy, I hope Mom comes pretty soon and I hope she brings something for supper, too. There's nothing in the refrigerator but some fried potatoes, a dish of sauerkraut, and a jar of dill pickles.

[*Enter* Henry *through door at back center, carrying the evening paper.*]

HENRY [*hanging coat and hat on the hall tree*]. How's everyone? [*Takes out watch.*] I guess I'm a little late tonight. It's nearly seven o'clock. Are you all through with supper?

JUNE *and* RICHARD. Oh, no. You see, we just got home—

GRANDMA [*interrupting*]. The children just got home, Henry, and Laura is downtown.

HENRY. Downtown? What's she doing downtown at this time of the night?

GRANDMA. She went to the Good Neighbor Club to help can applesauce for the orphanage. She said she'd bring something for supper.

HENRY. Well, let's put what we have on the table. Hard telling when she'll get here. [*Sighs and sits down in chair near the desk and begins to read the paper.*]

GRANDMA. All right. We'll get things going.

[*Exit* GRANDMA *and* JUNE, *left.* RICHARD *sits down at the table.*]

RICHARD [*putting elbows on the table*]. Football sure makes a guy hungry.

HENRY [*still reading the paper*]. Well, I guess you and June will be glad for a little vacation from school.

[*Enter* JUNE *with the silverware and dishes. She sets the table.*]

RICHARD. Yeah. But I can't practice any football. Every-

body in the neighborhood's goin' away. [*Pauses.*] Gee!
All that the fellows talked about in school today was
the turkey and cranberries and pie they're going to eat
tomorrow.

[*Exit* June, *left. Enter* Grandma *with a small bowl
of fried potatoes and a dish of sauerkraut.*]

Grandma [*setting the sauerkraut and potatoes on the
table*]. Come on, everybody. I guess we're ready to eat.

Enter June, *left, with a jar of dill pickles.* All *seat
themselves at the table and begin passing the food.*]

Richard. Same old sauerkraut and fried potatoes we had
for supper last night.

June. Cheer up. After this supper you'll be able to eat
all the more Thanksgiving dinner tomorrow.

Richard. I wish we'd have some food I like sometime.

June. You're too particular. You should learn to like all
the things that are good for you.

Richard. Well, I never heard of fried potatoes and sauerkraut building much muscle for anybody. [*Takes all of
the remaining potatoes.*]

Grandma. Richard, hadn't you better leave a few potatoes
for your mother?

Richard. No, she probably ate plenty of applesauce.

[*Enter* Laura, *through door at back center, carrying
a letter and a package.*]

LAURA. Hello, everyone. Am I late? [*Looks at wrist watch.*] My, it's way after seven! Where did the afternoon go? I didn't think it was so late. It seems like when a person gets busy working with a lot of other people the afternoon just slips away in no time at all. You should have seen the applesauce we canned! There were eight of us peeling the whole afternoon. I'm sure I have blisters on my hands. [*Puts package on desk. Pulls chair away from table and sits down. Puts letter in lap; takes off gloves, and looks at hands.*]

HENRY. Well, Laura, hadn't you better have something to eat now? Richard and June can go out to the car and bring in the groceries.

LAURA. No, no, you people go right ahead and finish eating. I couldn't eat a bite. We had a little lunch while we were canning. Mrs. Norton brought some of the most wonderful gelatin salad with nuts and pineapple and marshmallows in it—and just loads of whipped cream on top!

RICHARD [*sarcastically*]. We haven't had anything like that for so long that—

LAURA [*interrupting*]. And Mrs. Carson brought cookies. Oh, I do wish you could taste them! They had coconut and black-walnut meats in them. I must get the recipe. I would have brought each of you one, but there weren't any left. We girls just ate and ate! [RICH-

ARD *makes a face as he looks at the sauerkraut and potatoes on his plate and continues eating.* LAURA *picks up letter from her lap.*] Oh, I found this letter in the mailbox. [*Looks at envelope.*] From the telephone company! [*Opens envelope and reads letter.*] Oh, I know what it is. [*Reads.*] Your telephone bill is now three months overdue. If this bill is not paid by November [*names date before Thanksgiving*]—that's today—service will be discontinued. [*Looks startled.*]

HENRY. Well, there's nothing to worry about. You paid the bill today, didn't you?

LAURA. Well, no; not exactly.

HENRY. Not exactly! What do you mean? Either you paid it or you didn't pay it. I gave you the money for it last night.

LAURA. Well, you see it was this way. I was going into the telephone company office to pay the bill when I noticed in the window of Brock's store that they were having a sale on yarn. And I wanted to be sure to get some at the special price before they sold it all.

HENRY. Who are you knitting a sweater for this time?

LAURA. Each of us in the Good Neighbor Club is going to knit a sweater for the Flood Victims. [HENRY *nods.*] Well, I went in to Brock's knitting department and bought some of the most exquisite yarn. And when I came out the telephone company office was closed.

There was a sign saying they had closed at two o'clock because of the holiday. And besides, I'd spent all my money. So you see, I couldn't pay the bill, could I?

HENRY [*curtly*]. No, obviously you couldn't.

LAURA [*brightly*]. So then I just went right on to the Good Neighbor Club meeting and helped can the applesauce.

HENRY. I see.

RICHARD [*gets up from table and starts toward door*]. I'm through eating. June and I can bring in the groceries now. [*To* JUNE.] I'm going to carry the turkey.

[JUNE *gets up from the table.*]

GRANDMA [*starting to pick up the dishes*]. I do hope you were able to get a nice turkey, Laura. I'll help you make the dressing and we'll stuff it tonight.

LAURA. Turkey? [*Pauses.*] Oh, I'm sure you'll never forgive me—but I didn't get a turkey.

[RICHARD *and* JUNE *stop by the door at back center, amazed.*]

GRANDMA, HENRY, RICHARD, *and* JUNE [*in unison*]. Didn't get a turkey?

RICHARD. How can we have Thanksgiving without a turkey?

JUNE [*sitting on the davenport and almost crying*]. Oh, Mother, how could you? I don't see how anyone could forget to get a turkey.

GRANDMA. Your mother didn't say she *forgot* to get a
turkey, June. She just said she didn't get one. No
doubt she had a very good reason for not getting one.

HENRY [*looks doubtful; rises and stands by table*]. And
just what was your reason for not getting a turkey,
Laura?

LAURA. This is how it all happened. We didn't get
through canning applesauce till five-thirty. You see,
the applesauce—

RICHARD [*stamping his foot*]. Applesauce! It just doesn't
look as if we're going to have any Thanksgiving dinner
at all.

HENRY. Richard, please do not interrupt your mother.

LAURA. Well, as I said before, we didn't get through canning applesauce until five-thirty. But that was all
right, because the stores were all open until seven
tonight. Well, I went into all three of our meat
markets, and not one of them had a turkey left.

HENRY. Then, why didn't you get a duck or a chicken?

LAURA. A duck or a chicken? [*Pauses.*] A duck or a
chicken. Well, now isn't that the funniest thing. I
didn't think of that. I just thought I'd keep on trying
until I got a turkey, I guess.

HENRY [*looking very much disgusted*]. Well, what did
you do when you found out you couldn't get a turkey
at any of the meat markets?

LAURA. What did I do after that? [*Pauses.*] Now let me see. [*Pauses.*] What did I do after that? Oh, I know. I met Mrs. Cartright out in front of the Quality Meat Market and she said that her little Donald had the worst case of the whooping cough. He just whoops and whoops all the time at night, and Mrs. Cartright can't get any sleep at all.

HENRY. Laura—getting back to the subject of the turkey —did you try to get one anywhere else besides at the three markets?

LAURA. Oh, yes, I was just coming to that. After that I went into the new grocery that just opened, and they had some turkeys, but they wouldn't take a check, so I couldn't buy my things there. And by that time all the other downtown stores were closed, so I couldn't get anything at all.

JUNE. Well, I don't know what we'll do for Thanksgiving dinner. Just think. We won't have a turkey or a duck or a goose or even a chicken.

RICHARD. That's not the half of it. We won't have anything!

JUNE [*brightening*]. Oh, but I know what we can do! We can all eat at the restaurant! I saw a sign out in front of the Cozy Cupboard saying that you could get a turkey dinner there for seventy-five cents.

LAURA. Why, June! What a good idea! Why not?

HENRY. That will do, Laura. In all my forty-two years I have never eaten a Thanksgiving dinner at a restaurant, and I'm not going to begin now. Thanksgiving is a home day. We'll eat dinner here in this dining room or not at all.

LAURA. Yes, Henry. [*Murmurs of disappointment from* RICHARD *and* JUNE.] Now just control yourselves, all of you. I'll think of something to do.

[RICHARD *and* JUNE *look a little doubtful.*]

GRANDMA. Maybe I'll win a Thanksgiving dinner for us. Just this afternoon I bought a chance—

LAURA. A chance? Oh, Mamma, why are you always buying chances on things? You know you never win anything. Just last week you bought a chance on a cedar chest. And the week before that you bought a chance on a down comforter.

RICHARD. Well, maybe Grandma will win something sometime!

GRANDMA [*meekly*]. Remember, I almost won five hundred dollars at the movie on Bank Night last summer. My number was 869, and they called 868.

JUNE [*sadly*]. But you didn't really win, Grandma.

HENRY. Humph! And you probably never will. It's a silly waste of money, buying chances on things.

GRANDMA. Maybe we'll all be surprised sometime when I buy a chance. Somebody has to win, you know.

HENRY. Well, we'll see. [*To* LAURA.] Now, Laura, have you figured out just what you are going to do about our Thanksgiving dinner?

LAURA [*spontaneously*]. Oh! I have the best idea! We'll have a surprise Thanksgiving dinner! Richard and June, you go down to the Johnson Grocery on the corner and pick out just what you'd especially like for Thanksgiving dinner. Mr. Johnson told me last week that he'd have some nice chickens for Thanksgiving. You get one and pick out whatever else you want and the rest of us will be surprised. [*Enthusiastically.*] Won't that be fun? [ALL *agree in a surprised sort of way.*] Henry, give the children some money.

[HENRY *gives* RICHARD *a bill.* RICHARD *and* JUNE *put on wraps and go to door at back center.*]

RICHARD [*in doorway*]. You'll be surprised with what we bring back! [*Exit* RICHARD *and* JUNE.]

GRANDMA [*beaming*]. Now that was a nice idea, Laura.

HENRY [*looking doubtful*]. Time will tell.

[*Exit* LAURA, *left; puts on apron and returns.* LAURA *and* GRANDMA *stack the dishes and carry them out left and return.* LAURA *hums a tune as she works.*]

GRANDMA. There certainly aren't many dishes tonight.

HENRY. Say, Laura, do we have anything I can take? My stomach feels a little upset.

GRANDMA. I'll get some bicarbonate of soda. [*Exits left.*]

LAURA [*going over to* HENRY *and patting his hand*]. You poor dear. Are you getting one of those spells again? I do declare, I don't see why you have them so often. It seems like you have them oftener than you used to. It's funny. I never seem to get anything wrong with me. [GRANDMA *returns with a glass of water and a spoonful of soda and gives them to* HENRY. *After some hesitation and much persuasion on the part of the others,* HENRY *drinks the mixture.*] Mamma, I was just saying to Henry, I don't see why he gets these spells.

GRANDMA [*looking knowingly at* HENRY]. I wouldn't know either.

[*Enter* RICHARD *and* JUNE, *back center.* RICHARD *carries a very small package and* JUNE *carries two loaves of bread.*]

LAURA. Oh, children, you're not back so soon! And where is everything? Surely the whole surprise dinner isn't in that small package you're carrying, Richard!

RICHARD [*throwing package on table*]. I'm afraid it is. A half pound of hamburger.

JUNE. A half pound of hamburger was all the meat Mr. Johnson had left in the store. And he was all sold out of sweet potatoes and cranberries—and—[*almost crying*] everything that goes with a Thanksgiving dinner.

RICHARD [*taking the bread from* JUNE]. Mr. Johnson said we'd better take these two loaves of bread for stuffing.

HENRY. And just what do you think we're going to stuff?

CURTAIN

SCENE II

TIME: *Thanksgiving Day.*

SCENE: *Same as* SCENE I. GRANDMA *sits at right with a basket of darning.* JUNE *sits on the davenport manicuring her fingernails.* RICHARD *sits at the table working on a simple model airplane.* HENRY *is also at the table, working a newspaper crossword puzzle.*

HENRY. Now let me see—a nine-letter word meaning a red berry—I have it—*cranberry.* Only two more words, now. Next, a six-letter word meaning Thanksgiving fowl. That's *turkey*—t-u-r-k-e-y.

GRANDMA. Henry, I wish you'd quit working that crossword puzzle. Every word in it seems to have something to do with Thanksgiving dinner.

RICHARD. That's right, Dad. You've had *pumpkin* and *cranberry* and *turkey*, now. Boy, I've got such hunger pangs gnawin' in my stomach! A slice of dry toast makes a pretty slim breakfast.

JUNE [*irritably*]. Oh, hush, Richard; it's no worse for you than for the rest of us.

RICHARD. That's what you think! Everybody knows that girls don't get as hungry as boys.

GRANDMA. Now stop fussing—both of you. I do declare, I never saw two young ones act up the way you've been doing this morning.

HENRY. D-i-n-n-e-r, dinner. [*Folds up newspaper.*] That finishes it.

JUNE. What a Thanksgiving! I don't see why we can't eat dinner down at the Cozy Cupboard. Nobody else would have a Thanksgiving like this.

GRANDMA. That will do, June. You know how your father feels about eating at home on Thanksgiving.

[*Enter* LAURA, *left, taking off her apron.* HENRY *immediately opens the newspaper again and begins reading.* GRANDMA, JUNE, *and* RICHARD *keep busy, not looking up. There are a few seconds of silence.*]

LAURA [*hanging her apron over the back of the chair*]. Now all of you just wait until you see the luscious meat loaf I made!

RICHARD [*aside, with a sneer*]. With *half a pound* of hamburger.

LAURA. I always have said, if there's any one thing I can make better than most women, it's meat loaf. So many people just never can get their meat loaf seasoned right. And all it really takes to get things seasoned up right is a dash of this and a dash of that. Of course, I guess it's just about as bad to have food overseasoned as underseasoned. [JUNE *puts her manicuring articles in the desk and gets a magazine.*] Well, the dinner seems to be well on the way. I think I'll just get out my yarn and begin the sweater for the Flood Victims. [*Gets package from desk, opens it, and takes out white yarn. Holds it up and touches it.*] Isn't this the softest, wooliest, silkiest yarn you ever saw? Mmm! I do like the feel of it.

HENRY. Laura, did you say you were going to use that yarn to knit a sweater for one of the Flood Victims?

LAURA. Yes, everyone in the Good Neighbor Club is going to knit a sweater for a Flood Victim.

GRANDMA. Laura, how did you happen to choose white wool for the sweater?

LAURA. Oh, I forgot to tell you. All fifty of us in the Good Neighbor Club are knitting white ones. It was really my idea. I told the girls that I thought white was such a clean color and that if all the sweaters were light colored it would brighten things up. Everyone thought it was a marvelous idea. So we're all going to knit white sweaters.

HENRY [*impatiently*]. Laura, did it ever occur to you that all the Flood Victims are living in tents and that they might find it hard to keep white sweaters clean?

LAURA. Keep them clean? Why, I never thought of that. [*Pauses.*] Oh, well, now why should I worry about that? I always say we worry too much about other people's troubles. If people only wouldn't bother about trouble until it comes. [*Pauses.*] Now, let me see, where are my knitting needles?

GRANDMA. Here they are, Laura, in my sewing basket.

LAURA [*taking knitting needles from* GRANDMA]. For goodness sake! I wonder how they got in your basket. I don't remember putting them there. I just must find a special place for my knitting materials. [*Sits on davenport and begins knitting.*]

JUNE. Mother, what age person are you knitting your sweater for?

LAURA. What age person? [*Pauses, thinking.*] What age person? Well, what difference does it make?

GRANDMA. I should think it would make *some* difference, Laura. After all, you should know whether a child or a grownup will wear it so you'll know what size to make it.

LAURA. Oh, well, I'll just knit it and see what size it turns out to be. And it can go to whatever sized person it fits.

[HENRY *and* GRANDMA *look very disgusted.*]

JUNE [*looking up from magazine*]. Listen to this. It's an article about planning the Thanksgiving dinner. [*Reads.*] "Some people seem to believe that if they are to have a

dinner suitable for Thanksgiving they must have roast
turkey and sage dressing. Such people are overlooking a
chance to make the Thanksgiving dinner an unusual as
well as a pleasant experience in good eating. First, let us
consider the meat course. Did it ever occur to you that,
should you not be able to have a turkey or any other kind
of fowl, a piece of lamb shoulder or a piece of beef can
be shaped into a mock duck?"

RICHARD [*sarcastically*]. Does it say how you can shape
half a pound of hamburger into anything but half a
pound of hamburger?

GRANDMA [*sweetly*]. Go on, dear. Read the rest of it.

JUNE [*reading*]. "And must you always serve the same
kind of dressing with your dinner? If you usually make
a sage stuffing for your Thanksgiving fowl, why not
have oyster dressing this year?"

RICHARD [*goes to davenport and leans over back, looking
over* JUNE's *shoulder*]. Yeah, why not have oyster dressing? [*Pauses.*] My dear little magazine writer, you seem
to have forgotten that we have no oysters.

JUNE [*continues reading*]. "Or, if your family does not
care for oysters, make sausage and sweet potato stuffing.
Or the children may *prefer* a dressing made of prunes
and apples."

RICHARD. What this family *prefers* never seems to make
much difference.

LAURA. Now, isn't that a fine little article! It just shows that you don't have to have a turkey to have a Thanksgiving dinner. Some people think they have to have the same thing for Thanksgiving dinner year after year. They simply have no imagination.

RICHARD [*walking back to table, where he resumes work on his model airplane*]. Well, I don't know what the rest of you think about imagination. But I'd have a pretty hard time imagining that hamburger was anything but hamburger.

GRANDMA. Richard, I believe you've said enough about that now.

HENRY [*puts his hands in his pockets and walks about the room as he relates his experiences*]. You know, Thanksgiving's a great day—a great family day. The whole family being together on that day's a great experience. [JUNE *and* RICHARD *look very bored.*] You know, when I was a boy we always went to Aunt Hattie's and Uncle Jake's for—

JUNE *and* RICHARD [*interrupting, in unison*]. Thanksgiving dinner. Sometimes there was snow on the ground. Then you went in the sleigh. On one Thanksgiving Day the snow was so deep that you had to shovel a path part way for the sleigh to go through. And—

HENRY [*interrupting in self defense*]. That's not what I was going to say at all. I—er—I—well, I was going to tell about some of the special things we did at Aunt Hattie's and Uncle Jake's on Thanksgiving Day.

JUNE. We're sorry, Father. We were only teasing.

HENRY [*laughing*]. That's all right. I can take a joke.

JUNE. Go on, Father. Tell us what you were going to say.

HENRY [*stands in center of room*]. Well, I never saw anyone cook a Thanksgiving dinner the way Aunt Hattie used to. She must have started thinking about it in the middle of the summer.

First thing we got in the house, Aunt Hattie'd take us kids out in the kitchen. And I don't think any place ever smelled as good as Aunt Hattie's kitchen on Thanksgiving morning. Then Aunt Hattie'd give each of us a big piece of paper and tell us to write down all the things we could smell—or thought we could smell. "And I'll give a prize to the one with the list that's most nearly correct," Aunt Hattie would say. [*Chuckles.*]

RICHARD [*glumly*]. You wouldn't need a very big sheet of paper to write down all the kinds of food you could smell in our kitchen this morning. I could write *hamburger* on a postage stamp.

HENRY. We kids would write like mad—putting down everything we could think of that was good to eat. Pretty soon Aunt Hattie would say, "Time's up." Then each of us would read our list. Aunt Hattie would laugh and say, "Land Sakes! Some of those things on your lists don't even have any smell. But I'm going to give each of you a prize, anyhow." Then she'd give each of us a big stick of candy and warn us not to eat it before dinner or we'd spoil our appetites. [*Laughs.*] But of course we'd always nibble off the end of the stick when Aunt Hattie wasn't looking—and it didn't seem to spoil our appetites, either.

LAURA [*laughs*]. Henry, you used to do such strange things on Thanksgiving. Your Aunt Hattie must have been the funniest person.

RICHARD [*sarcastically*]. Not *funny*, Mom—just *human*.

JUNE. Tell us more about Thanksgiving at Aunt Hattie's, Father.

HENRY [*going over to table and illustrating his words by suitable gestures*]. Well, of course the most important part of the day's celebration was the dinner. Aunt Hattie'd put all the leaves in the big oak table; then she'd load it down with food. I don't see how the old table ever held up under so many platters and bowls and casseroles of the most tasty food you can imagine. When everything was on the table Uncle Jake would say, "Gather round, everybody! Victuals are on!" Then he'd take my arm and say, "Henry, you sit right here by your Uncle Jake. He'll see that you get plenty of turkey on your plate, and if your plate isn't big enough we'll see if Aunt Hattie can't find some sideboards." Then everyone would laugh.

RICHARD. You'd never need any sideboards for your plate around this place.

LAURA. Stop being so sarcastic, Richard.

HENRY [*leaning against table*]. When we'd get around the table, Aunt Hattie'd say, "Now nobody start eating till we've all told what we're thankful for." We'd start with Aunt Hattie and go clear around the table, everyone telling what he was thankful for. Uncle Jake was always last. He'd just say, "I'm thankful we don't have to wait any longer to eat. Everybody pitch in!"

JUNE [*earnestly*]. It must have been lots of fun to have Thanksgiving dinner at Aunt Hattie's and Uncle Jake's!

HENRY. It was! We always had turkey or goose and dressing and cranberries and apple salad and three or four vegetables, watermelon pickles, currant jelly, homemade rolls, and freshly-churned butter. And such pies! There was not only pumpkin pie, but mince pie and chocolate pie, too. I always had a hard time deciding which kind to eat.

RICHARD. Imagine having a chance to *decide* what to eat!

JUNE [*goes over by* GRANDMA *and sits on floor*]. Grandmother, what kind of Thanksgivings did you have when you were young?

GRANDMA. Well, we usually had a pretty good Thanksgiving when I was a girl. I remember that along about the first of October my mother would make a fruit cake and put it away until Thanksgiving. We children would always want a sample of it before Thanksgiving, but do you think my mother would let us have one? No sirree! She'd say, "No fruit cake until Thanksgiving —not even a teeny-tiny sliver."

LAURA. I wonder what they're going to have at the orphanage for Thanksgiving dinner today. Those poor little kiddies! I'll bet some of them don't even know what turkey tastes like.

RICHARD [*meaningfully*]. There are some children outside of the orphanage who are going to *forget* what it tastes like.

JUNE. Did you usually have turkey for your Thanksgiving dinner when you were a girl, Grandma?

GRANDMA. No, I can't say that we did. You see, we didn't raise turkeys on our farm. We always had chicken, though. Early in the fall my father would pick out a couple of our best chickens and say, "Now we'll put these two chickens in a pen alone and give them special feed so they'll be juicy and tender for Thanksgiving." And I declare, I've never tasted chicken more juicy and tender than those always were!

JUNE. I suppose you raised pumpkins on your farm, too— for pumpkin pies.

GRANDMA. Oh, we always had plenty of pumpkins for pumpkin pies on Thanksgiving. [*Pauses.*] Yes, we always had a good Thanksgiving dinner—that is, every year but one. And that was the year the house burned down. [GRANDMA *sniffs. Then* ALL *sniff.*] Say, do I smell something burning?

[ALL *sniff again.*]

LAURA [*dashing out left*]. Oh! It's the meat loaf! It's the meat loaf!

RICHARD [*nonchalantly*]. Well, there goes the half pound of hamburger. All up in smoke!

LAURA [*coming to door with a very small, very charred pan of meat loaf*]. Richard, I wish you'd stop calling this a half pound of hamburger. It isn't just a half pound of hamburger. There's nearly a loaf of bread in it—and some onion, too. And it isn't burned very much. Besides, I read in a magazine the other day that most of us don't get enough charcoal in our systems. [*Exits, left, with meat loaf.*]

RICHARD [*mumbling*]. The guy that wrote that article didn't know our family.

LAURA [*in doorway, smiling*]. Well, I guess about everything's ready now. June, you set the table and I'll get things on. [*Exit* JUNE, *left.* LAURA *puts a tablecloth on the table.* JUNE *brings in dishes and silver and a plate of bread.*] Now, everybody sit down. We're just about ready to eat. [GRANDMA *puts away darning.* HENRY, RICHARD, JUNE, *and* GRANDMA *stand behind their chairs.* LAURA *brings in the very small meat loaf on a very large platter. She sets it on the center of the table.* RICHARD *and* JUNE *look at it disapprovingly.* ALL *sit down.*] Now let's all do like Father did at Aunt Hattie's. We'll all think of one thing we're thankful for and tell it before we start eating. Henry, we'll start with you.

HENRY [*soberly*]. I'm thankful that our family has good health.

LAURA [*to* GRANDMA]. Mamma, you be next.

GRANDMA. Well, I'm thankful we all have a roof over our heads. That's a good deal these days.

HENRY. Richard!

RICHARD. I'm thankful—I'm thankful [*long pause—eyeing the meat loaf*] the only thing I can think of to be thankful for is that all of us will have plenty of charcoal in our systems.

   [*Doorbell rings.* LAURA, JUNE, *and* RICHARD *rise to go to door at back center.*]

HENRY [*to* JUNE *and* RICHARD]. Sit down. Your mother will go. It's probably for her, anyhow.

   [LAURA *opens the door, disclosing* JOE, *who carries a large covered box on his shoulder. He sets it in the doorway.*]

JOE. Good day, ma'am. I'm from the Schwartz Delicatessen—

LAURA [*interrupting*]. No, I don't want to buy anything today. I don't see why you people have to come around trying to take up subscriptions for magazines on a day like this. This is one day when people don't want to be bothered by—

JOE [*interrupting*]. But, ma'am, you don't understand. [*Starts to lift cover of box.*]

LAURA. No, I don't want a free sample of anything. I've lived long enough to know that those free samples that are given away are always paid for in the end. [*Starts to close door.*]

JOE [*putting his foot in the doorway*]. But ma'am, please let me explain. I'm from the Schwartz Delicatessen. I have a delivery to make.

LAURA. I'm sure you're mistaken. You haven't any delivery to make here, young man. I haven't bought anything from that delicatessen for three years. The last time I ordered anything from there was for a Good Neighbor Club meeting at my house. I ordered three chocolate cakes. And the afternoon of the meeting they delivered three *white* cakes. Imagine making a mistake like that!

JOE [*pushes the door open and steps inside*]. Madam, I did not come here to talk to you. And I'm not selling anything or giving away samples. I want to see Mrs. Jackson—Grandma Jackson!

GRANDMA [*rising and starting toward the door*]. I'm Grandma Jackson. Aren't you the boy who was here yesterday afternoon selling chances?

JOE [*grinning*]. That's right. We tried to call you on the phone this morning, but the telephone company said your phone is disconnected. Grandma Jackson, you had the lucky number! You won the ready-cooked Thanksgiving dinner. I've got it here in the box, piping hot. Where can I set the box?

[ALL *look very much amazed.*]

GRANDMA [*indicating middle of the floor*]. Why, I guess right here on the floor is as good a place as any.

[JOE *places box on the middle of the floor and takes out things and hands them to* GRANDMA, *who places them on the table. The turkey may be represented by a covered roaster. Many of the other things may be represented by covered bowls, etc.*]

JOE [*as he gives things to* GRANDMA]. Mashed potatoes. Cranberry sauce. Creamed peas. Waldorf salad. Candied sweet potatoes. Cauliflower. Fresh rolls. Butter. Currant jelly. Celery. Olives. Pickles. Pumpkin pie. And, last of all, the twenty-pound turkey! [*Puts empty box on shoulder.*] Well I guess you folks have plenty to be thankful for this Thanksgiving. So long. [*Exits.*]

[ALL *gather around the table.*]

JUNE [*hugging* GRANDMA]. I'm thankful for Grandma!

RICHARD [*lifts up roaster lid a little, takes out a big turkey leg, and takes a bite*]. And I'm thankful that Grandma took a chance!

CURTAIN

P O E M S

LONG AGO

Priscilla Prudence Patience Prim
Went out for a long walk.
She met a little Indian maid;
They stopped to have a talk.

"I like your beaded frock so much,"
The little Pilgrim said.
The other would have blushed if she
Had not been quite so red.

"Your snow-white collar is so fine,"
The Indian maid replied.
"I'll show you where my shells are hid,
And where my beads I hide."

So side by side the two walked on,
A very friendly pair,
And all their secrets there and then
They said that they would share.

PRETENDING

Peeking through the bushes
A redskin's face I see;
Through the bedroom window
An Indian's watching me.

Out there in the deep woods
Lurks a chief or two,
Ready there to scalp me
If I come in view.

Turkeys are a-roasting
In the fireplace hot;
And a lot of soft soap's
Bubbling in the iron pot.
You may think I'm fibbing,
Or talking rather wild.
You're wrong; I'm only playing
That I'm a Pilgrim child.

ONCE A YEAR

Once a year it might be fine
To check our luck—both yours and mine;
To count our blessings and to see
The good that's come to you and me.

Once a year it might be well
A little tale of thanks to tell,
For gratitude will hurt no man.
So be as thankful as you can.

AN INDUSTRIOUS PILGRIM

The Pilgrim lads of long ago
Worked very hard indeed;
They went out hunting every day
To get the food they'd need.
But I wouldn't call that work,
Going hunting with a gun;
If I could shoot deer and quail
I'd think it lots of fun.

The Pilgrim lads had to fish
And find clams by the sea;
If that were just my daily work,
How happy I would be.
Instead of carrying wood or coal,
I'd take my fishing hook
And with it catch some speckled trout
Down in the pasture brook.

The Pilgrim lads fought Indians.
I envy them, each one!
If I just had a chance I'll bet
I'd make the redskins run.
I wouldn't call it work at all,
To chase them with my rifle,

To get a dozen scalps or so
For me would be a trifle.

But then, I guess it always is
Work when you have to do
Tasks pointed out by someone else
And handed then to you.
A Pilgrim lad might think it fun
Running errands to the store
And doing the many other things
That pile up by the score.

I guess it is all right to say
The Pilgrim lads worked well,
For many tales about their deeds
Our storybooks do tell.
I wonder if the books someday
Will speak of me and you
And tell the little children then
Of all the work we do.

THANKSGIVING GREETINGS

If I were a Pilgrim girl
Of the long, long ago,
I would love Thanksgiving
Very much, I know.

But I am a modern girl;
Still I hold it very dear.
I am happy as can be
Because Thanksgiving's near.

WELCOME, THANKSGIVING

Welcome, Thanksgiving!
I am glad you are here;
You're the gayest time
Of the whole long year.

You tell us of Pilgrims
Who helped found our land,
And you bring us a day
That is ever so grand.

MY PIECE

I have a little piece to speak
About Thanksgiving Day;
They said I couldn't learn much
But a short one I could say.

So here it is: "I wish you
The best Thanksgiving joy."

Now don't you think I did fine
For such a little boy?

TO A "T"

Thanksgiving and turkey,
Both start with a "T";
They are two things
That exactly suit me.

So I know what it means
When folks say to me
That something or other
Suits them to a "T."

PILGRIM NAMES

I like the name Priscilla,
Because it seems to speak
Of days when Pilgrim Fathers
Their freedom aimed to seek.
It tells of loyal mothers
Who worked from morn till night
To keep their families well,
And fed and clothed aright.

I like the name John Alden,
Because it rings so true;

It tells of many noble things
Strong-hearted men can do.
It speaks of sacrifice and love;
It brings a thought of strife,
Such as the early settlers faced
In the land that gave free life.

I like the simple Pilgrim names;
They lack all frills and fads.
They were suited to the grownups
And the littlest girls and lads.
I wonder how our names will sound
To those who of our deeds may read;
Perhaps they'll think them odd,
Or hardly give them heed.

THE TURKEY'S LAMENT

"Oh, dear!" said the turkey,
"I think I shall die,
For I've heard it said
That Thanksgiving's nigh."

"My sakes!" said the cook,
Who in the window sat,

"That old turkey gobbler
Is really nice and fat."

"Oh, my!" said Old Turk,
"I know what's my fate.
How I regret now
All the corn that I ate."

He thought and he thought
Of what he could do.
He ran to the woods
And in a tree he flew.

But he soon became hungry
And said with a sigh,
"I'll hurry right back
And peacefully die."

But when he returned
He saw, to his glee,
The cook had just killed
Young turkeys three.

And he heard her say,
When he came close enough,
"I'm glad I missed Old Turk,
For he'd surely be tough."

ALL FOR THANKSGIVING DAY

The pumpkin gloated as he sat
Upon the garden wall:
"A pumpkin pie I'm going to be—
And much enjoyed by all!
I'm thankful now to be of use
Upon Thanksgiving Day!
I'm of importance to the feast,
The people always say."

The scarlet leaves were like a flame
As they blew down the way.
"We're thankful we'll help decorate
Upon Thanksgiving Day!
Right in the center of the feast,
Right where the turkey reigns,
Our scarlet beauty will be found—
Reward for all our pains."

The orchard spoke, "I will be there,
And thankful am I, too,
That all the fruits of my domain
Will prove their merits true.
They grew just for Thanksgiving Day
And ripened in the sun.
And when the feast is at an end
May folks cry out 'Well done.'"

Then all the yield of meadows green,
And of the valleys deep
Spoke up and said that they would too
Their share of praises reap.
And all cried joyously aloud—
The same words did they say—
"We grew and bloomed and ripened well
Just for Thanksgiving Day."

FOR THESE I'M THANKFUL

I'm thankful for my health and home,
And lovely woodlands where I roam.
I'm thankful for each word of cheer
That I receive from friends so dear.

I'm thankful for my parents' love,
And for God's help from up above;
I'm thankful for things small and grand,
But most for America, my land.

I'm thankful that to school I go
To learn the things that I should know;
I'm thankful for teachers kind and true
Who help me by the work they do.

I'm thankful for food and for clothes, too,
And for things old and for things new.
I'm thankful for seas with shores of sand,
But most for America, my land.

I'm thankful for a flag that's bright
With stars that ever speak of right.
I'm thankful for men with hearts of steel
Whose service to the country is very real.

I'm thankful for the people of long ago
Who helped build this land we all love so.
And I'm thankful for the Pilgrim band
Who helped found America, my land.

HOW STILL THE FORESTS

How still the forests must have been
Upon the day the Pilgrims came.
How wide the meadows must have stretched
Across a land without a name.

How strange the soil 'neath Pilgrim feet!
How gray the clouds that hung above!
And not a roof to shelter them;
But what they had was hope and love.

They loved their faith and principles;
And they had prayer to lead them on,
And hope that all their sufferings
Would bring a new and perfect dawn.

How fearful must the land have looked;
To that the Pilgrims gave no heed.
They prayed and sang aloud their songs,
Safe in their strong and boundless creed.

INDIAN SUMMER

The air is growing hazy now;
The fields are looking drear;
There is a lonesome feeling
Around this time of year.
If you look at the horizon
You'll see dancing spirits clear;
By all these signs you'll know
That Indian summer's here.

The leaves of trees are bright
And falling to the ground;
The cornstalks stand in shocks,
While pumpkins lie around.

The birds are flying southward,
No songster can be found;
The winds blow o'er the prairies
With wailing, wistful sound.

Indeed, it's Indian summer,
When spirits come once more,
To dance across the acres
Where they hunted years before.
If you look for them you'll see them
Passing by your very door;
For it's lovely Indian summertime
With its magic Indian lore.

NUTTING TIME

Yes, I know the ways are rugged,
And the nuts grow 'way up high;
I know the hour is getting late,
And that clouds are in the sky.

But when I am out nutting,
With my basket on my arm,
I simply cannot turn toward home
Till I have searched the farm.

My dog is quite as glad as I
When nutting time is here;
He sees me starting on the trip
And follows me far and near.

A rabbit he may find to chase,
Perhaps a pheasant comes in view;
There are many things right now
For boys and dogs to do.

So you do not need to warn me
Of the tiredness I will feel,
Nor of the coming rainstorm,
That may upon me steal.

Oh, the joy I get from nutting
Pays me well for all I do;
If you'll only try it someday,
I'm sure you'll feel it, too.

SNOWFLAKES AND LEAVES

This morning I stood at my window,
And saw flutter down from the sky
The first snowflakes of the season,
That came on the ground to lie.

But scarce had they touched the earth,
When quickly they melted away;
I thought it was a dreadful shame
When they wanted so much to play.

Just then a number of autumn leaves
Flew down past my windowpane.
What I overheard them saying
Made the matter to me quite plain.

"Those snowflakes have a lot of nerve
To come so early," said one;
"We'll just have the earth melt them all away,
So we can finish our fun."

"The months for the snowflakes are coming,"
Another leaf said with a sigh,
"But everyone knows that October
Is the month for the leaves to fly."

HARVEST

Harvest means labor brought to the flower;
Harvest means fruit of the well-spent hour.
And also it means that day when we praise
The Plymouth settlers of Pilgrim days.

Harvest means fruit jars placed in a row—
All of the orchard's gifts that we know.
And also it means a good word we'll say
To honor the Pilgrims this Thanksgiving Day.

AUTUMN SPIRITS

There's a mystic, magic something
Hovering in the air tonight;
There's an eerie, scary something
Of things just out of sight.

People step a bit more lightly
As they go along the walk;
People speak a little softer
When they pause to chat or talk.

I think I know the reason now,
Why these strange things we hear;
I think I know the secret
Of this thrilling time of year.

These are spirits of the summer,
That we hear and faintly see;
They are visions of months past
That haunt both you and me.

So I still will step more lightly
Till the autumn days are past;
I still will speak more softly
Till King Winter comes at last.

Then I'll know those summer spirits
Have no right to hold their sway;
Then I'll turn from autumn's musings
To winter's wholesome, happy play.

THE UNSEEN GUEST

The sky and water formed a wall
That gave no hint of what might lay
Beyond for those who dared sail forth
Upon that long-gone famous day.

The stars were silent in the skies;
The winds that blew spoke not a word;
And on the "Mayflower's" darkening deck
Only the Pilgrims' prayers were heard.

But at their side throughout the trip
An unseen guest was on that boat,
And when the "Mayflower" reached our land
With steady hand the strange guest wrote.

The fingers wrote of Pilgrim days;
They told of suffering and a creed;
To all the hardships they gave note
That you and I might someday read.

The unseen guest was History—
Silently come without display.
In memory of the Pilgrim folk
We read our history books today.

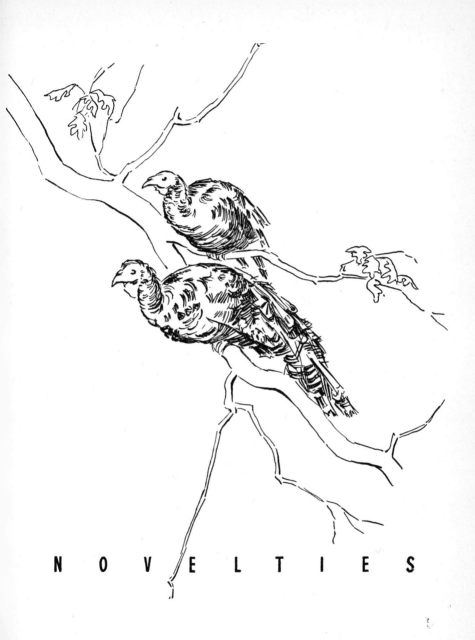

NOVELTIES

THE MAYFLOWER COMPACT

CHARACTERS

PILGRIM LEADER
OTHER PILGRIMS, *any number*

COSTUMES

ALL: *Typical Pilgrim costumes.*

SCENE: *On board the "Mayflower." LEADER at a table with the Mayflower Compact ready to be read. OTHER PILGRIMS gathered about, men in the foreground.*

LEADER. The Mayflower Compact is ready to be signed. I will read it to you and then those who wish may sign their names before we leave the good ship "Mayflower." Every group of people needs a set of rules to provide for its welfare, and this is our first step. Are you ready that I shall read it to you?

OTHER PILGRIMS. Ready.

LEADER. "On the Mayflower, 1620. In the name of God, Amen. We whose names are hereunder written, the loyal subjects of our dread sovereign, King James, by the grace of God, of Great Britain, France, and Ireland, King, Defender of the Faith, etc., having undertaken for the glory of God and advancement of the Christian Faith, and honor of our King and Country, a voyage to

163

plant the first colony in the northern parts of Virginia, do by these presents solemnly and mutually, in the presence of God and one another, covenant and combine ourselves together into a civil body politic for our better ordering and preservation and furtherance of ends aforesaid; and by virtue hereof to enact, constitute, and frame such just and equal laws, ordinances, acts, constitutions, and offices, from time to time, as shall be thought most meet and convenient for the general good of the colony, unto which we promise all due submission and obedience."

OTHER PILGRIMS. We will sign that now. [*They come forward and write their names.*]

LEADER. It is well done. May we in our new home find peace and safety.

CURTAIN

PILGRIM PEOPLE

CHARACTERS

CAPTAIN MILES STANDISH   ELDER BREWSTER

JOHN ALDEN   PILGRIM GIRL

PRISCILLA   PILGRIM BOY

COSTUMES

CAPTAIN MILES STANDISH: *Military costume typical of his period. See page 4.*

JOHN ALDEN: *Typical Pilgrim costume.*

PRISCILLA: *Dress made with long sleeves and long, full skirt, with white collar and cuffs. Carries her knitting.*

ELDER BREWSTER: *Typical Pilgrim costume with a long black coat or cape. Carries a Bible.*

PILGRIM GIRL *and* PILGRIM BOY: *Costumes similar to those worn by adult Pilgrims.*

SCENE: *Before the curtain. Enter* CAPTAIN MILES STANDISH. *He comes to center of stage.*

CAPTAIN MILES STANDISH.

> I am Miles Standish,
> A soldier of fame;
> In the Plymouth colony
> Men honor my name.
> My army is small,
> But true to the core.
> To defend our village
> Each able man swore.

> [*Enter* JOHN ALDEN.]

JOHN ALDEN.

> I am John Alden,
> A lover so true;
> I'm known far and wide
> For the courting I do.

I've found in this land
A home of my own
That's proving to be
The happiest I've known.

[*Enter* PRISCILLA.]

PRISCILLA.

I am Priscilla,
A fair little miss,
Who with my cheer
Give people much bliss.
To spin and weave
I had to learn,
For to many such tasks
Pilgrim folk have to turn.

[*Enter* ELDER BREWSTER.]

ELDER BREWSTER.

I am Elder Brewster,
A man of prayer,
Who preaches the gospel
In this new land so fair.
To keep faith with God
We came over the sea,
That to worship in peace
We might be free.

[*Enter* PILGRIM GIRL *and* PILGRIM BOY.]

PILGRIM GIRL.

> I am a little girl
> Of the Pilgrim days.
> I am afraid you will
> Laugh at my ways.
> I know how to make soap,
> To gather clams, and to fish.
> I eat my plain meals
> From a wooden dish.

PILGRIM BOY.

> I am a Pilgrim boy
> From the long ago.
> How to shoot a rifle
> I have to know.
> I am very busy
> The whole day through.
> There are many tasks
> For us Pilgrims to do.

ALL [*together*].

> We are Pilgrim people
> From the Massachusetts shore.
> We've come to help you all enjoy
> Thanksgiving Day the more.

[*Exit* ALL.]

TEN LITTLE BUNNIES

CHARACTERS

TEN BUNNIES, *primary children*

COSTUMES

BUNNIES: *Each child carries a large picture of a rabbit or wears a rabbit cap with long pointed ears.*

SCENE: *Stage is bare. One BUNNY enters at a time and speaks. As the other BUNNIES enter, they form a line across the front of stage.*

FIRST BUNNY.

> One little bunny
> In the woodland bare;
> He can easily tell
> That winter's there.

SECOND BUNNY.

> Two little bunnies
> Looking all about;
> They know full well
> Hunters will be out.

THIRD BUNNY.

> Three little bunnies
> Not afraid of cold;
> Of many woodland dangers
> They have been told.

FOURTH BUNNY.

> Four little bunnies,
> Pretty as you please;
> See them hop about
> With graceful ease.

[*All the* BUNNIES *hop about the stage two or three times.*]

FIFTH BUNNY.

> Five little bunnies,
> Oh, so very gay;
> You'll see them near
> Every autumn day.

SIXTH BUNNY.

> Six little bunnies
> Who like frosty air;
> If you visit cornfields,
> You'll see them there.

SEVENTH BUNNY.

> Seven little bunnies,
> As lively as can be;
> See how they skip about,
> So happy and so free.

[ALL *skip about the stage.*]

EIGHTH BUNNY.

> Eight little bunnies,
> Glad to be alive;
> They hope the hunters
> Will not soon arrive.

NINTH BUNNY.

> Nine little bunnies
> Frolicking all about;
> They are very happy
> To be running out.

TENTH BUNNY.

> Ten little bunnies!
> What a jolly crowd!
> They have lots of fun,
> But seldom are they loud.

[The BUNNIES *join hands and hop about the stage in a circle. They stop near center front of stage.*]

ALL.

> Ten little bunnies,
> Dancing without fear;
> They know they're safe
> When Thanksgiving's here!

[*Exit* ALL, *happily.*]

AN AUTUMN FROLIC

CHARACTERS

LEAVES
TREES   } *two or more children*
BERRIES   *representing each*
BREEZES

COSTUMES

LEAVES: *Children's clothes are decked with bright paper leaves.*

TREES: *Small branches of pine trees are fastened to the children's clothes.*

BERRIES: *Bright-colored paper berries are fastened to the children's clothing.*

BREEZES: *Flowing robes of blue material.*

SCENE: *Stage is bare. Enter* LEAVES, *hand in hand.*

LEAVES. We are the bright leaves.

[*Enter* TREES.]

TREES. And we are the trees.

[*Enter* BERRIES.]

BERRIES. We are the bright berries.

[*Enter* BREEZES.]

BREEZES. And we are the breeze.

LEAVES. We brighten the dull earth.

TREES. We spread gladsome mirth.

BERRIES. We feed the birds gay.

BREEZES. We help you on your way.

[ALL *join hands and dance lightly around the stage.* TREES AND BREEZES *then step to the front of stage.*]

TREES *and* BREEZES.

> We are the trees
> And we are the breeze.

[BERRIES *and* LEAVES *step to front of stage.*]

BERRIES *and* LEAVES.

> We are the berries
> And we are the leaves.

[ALL *join hands and dance around the stage. If desired, an autumn dance may be arranged and lively music may be played.*]

CURTAIN

THANKSGIVING ACROSTIC

CHARACTERS

TWELVE CHILDREN

NOTE: *Each child carries one letter of the word "Thanksgiving." Letters may be cut from brown construction paper and decorated with red.*

SCENE: *Before the curtain.* CHILDREN *enter in order and form a line across front of stage. Letters are held at an even height so that the completed word may be read easily by the audience.*

FIRST CHILD.

> T   is for the turkey,
> So big and brown.
> I hope ours will be
> The finest in town.
> When it is roasted
> And put on the table
> I am going to eat
> As much as I'm able.

SECOND CHILD.

> H   is for the homecoming
> For our family dear,
> Who hasten homeward
> When Thanksgiving's here.
> We greet everyone
> With a gay, happy smile,
> For to be with us now
> They traveled many a mile.

THIRD CHILD.

> A   is for the Almighty God
> Whom we thank this day

For giving us the blessings
We find upon our way.
As we receive His many gifts
At this season of Thanksgiving,
Let us try to use them
In the right kind of living.

FOURTH CHILD.

N   is for the neighbors kind
Who share in our joy.
They help to spread cheer
To each good girl and boy,
While we in our turn
Help them with a will;
We'll gladly run errands
Or their woodboxes fill.

FIFTH CHILD.

K   is for the big kitchen
Where our dinner is cooked;
'Twould fill you with awe
If but in it you looked.
The tables are loaded with
Fine things for the day,
While the shelves are heavy
With their tempting display.

SIXTH CHILD.

S is for the snowflakes first
 That may flutter down
 As the close of November
 Comes hastening 'round.
 These first signs of winter
 Fill our hearts with cheer,
 For we have jolly times
 When old winter is here.

SEVENTH CHILD.

G is for the good will
 That abounds at this time;
 The spirit of thankfulness
 Invades every clime.
 The spirit of good will
 Is with us this day;
 We hope for one year
 It will choose to stay.

EIGHTH CHILD.

I is for the great industry
 Of the Pilgrims of old
 Who came to this new world
 With hearts brave and bold.

They worked all the day,
And many a night through,
To help settle this new land
Where pleasures were few.

NINTH CHILD.

V   is for the vigorous life
These forefathers led;
They were much out of doors
And on plain food were fed.
Their bodies grew strong
With Dame Nature's kind aid.
If we follow their example
Our weakness will fade.

TENTH CHILD.

I   is for the Indians
Who, though at times wrong,
Were a brave race of people,
Both healthy and strong.
On the first Thanksgiving
They dined in Plymouth town
Where a very fine dinner
On the table they found.

ELEVENTH CHILD.

   N is for wonderful Nature,
      Who blesses us with plenty;
      Without her kind aid
      Many would be hungry.
      The fields and vineyards
      Yield their richness rare
      To help make a finer
      Thanksgiving bill of fare.

TWELTH CHILD.

   G is for the gaiety bright
      That this season brings;
      With laughter and happiness
      Every household rings.
      All hearts are happy now
      Because the harvest is stored;
      Safely in bins and barns
      Nature's yield has been poured.

ALL [*together*].

      So we have spelled Thanksgiving,
      The thankful day of all the year.
      We hope it will bring to each one
      The best of heartfelt cheer.

        [*Exit* ALL.]

THE HARVEST KING

CHARACTERS

HARVEST KING	PUMPKIN	ONION
APPLE	CORN	CABBAGE
NUT	GRAPE	PARSNIP

COSTUMES

HARVEST KING: *Gold crown and a cape.*

APPLE, NUT, PUMPKIN, CORN, GRAPE, ONION, CABBAGE, PARSNIP: *Each carries a large picture of the fruit or vegetable he represents.*

[*Enter* HARVEST KING.]

HARVEST KING.

>I am king of the harvest,
>Ruler of all that we grow.
>The secret of plowing
>And gathering crops I know.
>I welcome rain and sunshine
>As gifts from God above;
>I use the blessings that he gives
>From out his bounteous love.
>
>From out of the fields and gardens
>I've called my subjects today,
>That they may tell their story
>Each in his own plain way.

They are all known to you;
You will welcome them, I know.
In all of our fair country
You'll see them where'er you go.

APPLE.

I am your friend, the apple,
So shiny, bright, and red;
People are usually healthy
If on me they're daily fed.
I have a host of flavors
To please you, every one.
Without me jolly harvesttime
Would lose a lot of fun.

NUT.

I am one of the sweet nuts
That grow so wild and free.
You're almost sure to find me
On hickory or walnut tree.
Just when the frost is cracking,
It's time to look for me.
The harvesting of the nut crop
Is as gay as it can be.

PUMPKIN.

I am one of the pumpkins
That grows out on the vine;

I make those luscious pies
On which you like to dine.
I make the jack-o'-lanterns
That frighten people so.
Without a pumpkin harvest
You'd miss a lot, I know.

CORN.

I am a waving cornstalk fair
With ears so big and yellow.
The men begin my husking
When the moon is full and mellow.
The cribs will soon be bursting
With the harvest wealth I give;
Without my generous helpfulness
It would be hard to live.

GRAPE.

The grapes of richest purple
In the fall are gathered in.
Among the many harvest fruits
A prize they'd surely win.
When the air is growing cooler
And the birds have flown away,
The grapes are very, very good
On a bright and crispy day.

HARVEST KING.

> Now from the vegetable garden
> Some of my subjects we greet.
> On tables in the wintertime
> They very often meet.
> They give you health and pleasure
> Throughout the winter days.
> You like their tasty flavors
> In many, many ways.

ONION.

> I am one of your strongest friends,
> An onion tried and true.
> I come in yellow, red, and white,
> And try to please all of you.
> I make a sandwich good to eat
> Upon a winter's day,
> Although there may be some who think
> I drive their friends away.

CABBAGE.

> I am a head of cabbage white
> From out the garden's store.
> I still am full of goodness
> Though summertime is o'er.

In salads or in the kettle
I please the folks I meet.
The winter will be merrier
With cabbage fine to eat.

PARSNIP.

All winter long a parsnip
Can stay within the ground;
But what fine food I am for you
When at last I'm found!
All nestled in a frying pan,
With butter sizzling near,
I am the choice of everyone
When dinnertime is here.

HARVEST KING.

I'm sure we have convinced you
That harvesttime is best,
Although you may like summer
And spring and all the rest.
There's something in the autumn
That seems to softly say,
"The harvest king is waiting
To brighten up your way."

ALL [*in unison*].

> So now we'll go away
> With a very brief adieu,
> But before the winter days are past
> We will meet each of you.
> And if upon the table
> Our faces you should spy,
> Just nod and say a "howdy"
> Before each of us you try.

CURTAIN

THE MONTHS

CHARACTERS

TWELVE CHILDREN, *representing the twelve months*

COSTUMES

No costumes are necessary. However, if desired, children may be dressed to symbolize the months they represent: for example, the child representing JANUARY *might wear a snow suit; the child representing* DE-CEMBER *might wear red and green clothing; etc. Each child carries a card bearing the name of the month he represents.*

SCENE: *Before the curtain. The* MONTHS *enter and form a semicircle across the stage.* JANUARY *goes to the left front corner and* DECEMBER *to the right front corner. The others take their places in order between. The cards are held out in front so that they may be plainly seen.*

JANUARY.

> January brings the glad New Year
> With resolutions good and true,
> But I wonder how many of them
> Are ever kept by any of you.
>
> Coasting and skating on every side
> Are sure to meet your eye,
> When January's snowy days
> Are slowly passing by.

FEBRUARY.

> February is the birthday month
> Of Lincoln and Washington;
> And with this month's most famous days
> St. Valentine's brings its fun.
>
> Birthdays of Lowell and Longfellow
> Deserve a place of honor here;
> There are a host of real holidays
> When February's here.

MARCH.

>March is the helter-skelter month
>That brings the wind a-blowing;
>What capers the next day will bring
>There is no way of knowing.
>
>St. Patrick's Day right here we find
>And don our clothes of green,
>So on that jolly holiday
>We may be rightly seen.

APRIL.

>April is the month of showers,
>Of battles royally won;
>When its breezes gently blow
>With our kites we have great fun.
>
>We watch for the first flower
>That dares to show its head;
>And almost hold our breath with fear
>That all the plants are dead.

MAY.

>May is the month of memories
>Of soldiers who are dead;
>And for some dear departed one
>Each person bows his head.

It brings the day that's set aside
To honor Mother dear;
The flowers burst into welcome bloom
When May comes creeping near.

JUNE.

The jolly, joyful month of June
Brings Flag Day, and swimming, too;
What a wealth of things there are
For girls and boys to do.

The bees begin their humming tune
And bird songs fill the air;
In all the year around, I think,
There is no month so fair.

JULY.

July brings our Independence Day
With all its fun and noise;
I'm sure that this day always is
The choice of all the boys.

'Tis haying time and clover time,
And the air is sweet indeed;
The sun shines warmly overhead,
No shoes or socks we need.

AUGUST.

> Now comes the month for Caesar named.
> I think you will agree
> That the lazy days of August
> Just suit both you and me.
>
> The harvest now is ready,
> And the reapers are in the field;
> While the acres seem contented
> And proud of their generous yield.

SEPTEMBER.

> The goldenrod of September
> Is something to gladden the eye;
> Workers look forward to a rest
> As Labor Day draws nigh.
>
> The leaves begin to slightly flutter,
> As if looking for some guest;
> Jack Frost soon will be calling
> And in colors they'll be dressed.

OCTOBER.

> Columbus Day in gay October
> Is one day worthy of mention,
> And Halloween follows it close by
> To claim its share of attention.

The brightness of the leaves and flowers,
And hazy Indian-summer days,
The fullness of the nut trees
Will haunt our mem'ry always.

NOVEMBER.

Now comes the month of honor
That we're thinking of today;
The month that finds a thankful heart
In all it meets along the way.

November—the month of Thanksgiving!
Hail it and greet it with joy,
For it gladdens the heart of every man
And pleases each girl and boy.

DECEMBER.

December brings our Christmastime,
And Christmas brings a loaded tree
With gifts for every single one,
And lots and lots of company.

It is a time of joy and fun
For everyone concerned;
It is the happiest holiday
To which our thoughts are turned.

ALL.

> Hail to the whole year round!
> Each month brings something new;
> Each brings something of beauty,
> And each happy days for you.

> Hail to the whole year round!
> All honor its months, every one!
> Each has a time for earnest work,
> And each has a time for fun.

[*Exit* ALL.]

GYPSY DANCE

CHARACTERS

EIGHT GYPSY DANCERS

COSTUMES

GYPSY DANCERS: *Girls are dressed in bright skirts and blouses. Each wears around her neck a bright scarf, which she later uses in the dance. Several bracelets, and beads and earrings should be worn. Ornaments which look like brass may be made of metal paper. Little bells may be fastened on the costumes so that a tinkling accompanies the movements.*

Music *and* Steps: *Any gay music of gypsy-dance nature may be used, as the movements of the dance are lively and spirited, accompanied by head movements in keeping with the steps.*

The First Gypsy Dancer *comes to the center front of stage and recites before the dance music starts.*

First Gypsy Dancer.

> I am the queen of the gypsies.
> From out of the woodland bowers
> I will call some of my maidens,
> The fairest of woodland flowers.
> We shall dance here before you
> Just as in camp we do.
> So forget the busy world about,
> And visit scenes wild and new.
>
> With only the blue sky above us,
> Where stars come peeping through,
> With the lively gypsy music gay
> We'll do steps both old and new.
> So come in mind to the woodlands,
> In the light of the campfire's rays,
> And dance with us in our gladness
> During the happy autumn days.

> [*Exit* First Gypsy Dancer.]

MOVEMENT 1. All dance onto stage in single file. The hands are on the hips and heads sway to and fro in time with the music. The leader comes to the center front of stage, turns quickly toward back of stage, and dances to center back. The others follow.

MOVEMENT 2. From center back of stage the leader dances to the back right corner and then turns sharply about and dances to front corner. The others follow, but those near the center of line remain nearer the back of stage so that a semicircle is formed. The left hand is now placed on the hip, the right one curved over the head, and each dancer turns lightly about in place, to the right.

MOVEMENT 3. Others sway to and fro in time with the music, as those from the ends dance to the center front of stage, lock arms, and circle to the right. After they circle, the others move nearer the corners of stage to make room for couple that has just finished circling to step in at center.

MOVEMENT 4. The remaining couples then repeat above movement.

MOVEMENT 5. The two couples nearest the center of the group dance to the center front, turn left, and dance across front and down side of stage. Remaining two couples dance to the center front, turn right, and dance across front and down side of stage. Lines turn to face each other. All in both lines dance to center, lock arms, place free hand on hip, and circle to right, then return to side of stage.

MOVEMENT 6. The dancers from the back and front corners dance to center of stage. Those from opposite corners join hands over the hands of the other couple. All four circle to the right, then return to side.

MOVEMENT 7. The others then dance to center of stage and repeat above movement.

MOVEMENT 8. The two nearest back of stage dance to center back, up center together, and across front. Others follow so that a line is formed across the front of stage.

MOVEMENT 9. All sway from right to left for four counts. Then both hands are held high over the head as dancers turn lightly to right. Hands are again placed on hips while the dancers sway from right to left.

MOVEMENT 10. With turning, circling motions all dance toward back of stage, where they pause and face audience. All sway from right to left in time with music. Those from the end dance to center front of stage, and there dance around each other and return to place, while the others sway to and fro in time with music.

MOVEMENT 11. The others repeat the movement until all have danced about at center. Then all place hands lightly on the shoulders of the one next in line and dance to front of stage. All raise arms high over the head and circle to right.

MOVEMENT 12. Those at end of the line dance slowly toward front of stage so that as large semicircle as there is room for is formed. With both hands all take hold of scarf worn around the neck, leaving it around the neck, and extend scarf as far to the sides as it reaches. As this is being done all circle lightly twice to the right.

MOVEMENT 13. All hold one end of scarf in right hand at center back of neck. Scarf is then extended to side and down as far as possible with left hand, and in this position all dance toward front of stage and around stage, returning in same semicircular position as when movement started.

MOVEMENT 14. Scarf is now lifted over the head and held in both hands in front of body. The hands are extended apart as far as scarf and stage room permit. All dance lightly toward the front of stage in semicircular position. Those at center dance near the front, so that almost a straight line is formed. All turn about to right before those at center dance back nearer back of stage.

MOVEMENT 15. The scarf is placed around the neck. One end is held in each hand, slightly in front of the body, as the dancers come to front of stage to form a straight line. Hands are extended high over the head as dancers turn to the right.

MOVEMENT 16. All sway from right to left in time with the music for four counts. All turn to the right, dance around stage, and exit.

[*All the movements may be repeated before the dancers leave stage, if desired.*]

MARCH OF THE SCARECROWS

CHARACTERS

Eight Scarecrows

COSTUMES

Scarecrows: *Boys are dressed in very old, ragged clothes and slouch hats. They carry old brooms. False faces are worn.*

Music *and* Steps: *Any slow march music may be used. All movements are of a listless, shuffling nature.*

Movement 1. The scarecrows enter in single file. The broom is held over left shoulder with left hand. Right hand swings listlessly at side. They march in along back of stage until all are in line at back of stage. Here they pause for a moment still facing the side of stage. They mark time slowly while they pause. They then turn abruptly about and march entirely around stage in opposite direction.

Movement 2. When leader has gone completely around stage he pauses in the corner at back until all are in line across back of stage. Then all face front of stage and hold the broom in front of the face with both hands. All march to front of stage.

Movement 3. Others mark time while the two at center back toward back of stage. When they are almost at back of stage, they pause and mark time while the two who are now nearest the center of stage back to within a few feet in front and to the side of them. These now mark time while the next couple back a few feet. Those nearest the corner in front line remain in position.

MOVEMENT 4. All take broom in right hand and extend it toward right side of stage; with four jerky movements return it to front of body, still using only the right hand. The left hand is at the side. All repeat the same movement. As broom is returned to front of body it is slightly raised and lowered four times and gradually brought toward the center of body.

MOVEMENT 5. All take broom in right hand and repeat above movement.

MOVEMENT 6. Broom is grasped in both hands and extended toward front of the stage. The handle is pointed toward floor. With broom still in this position all turn about slowly twice to right. All pause and mark time for four counts before turning about slowly twice to left.

MOVEMENT 7. Couple nearest back of stage take broom in right hand and march back to center front of stage. The next couple nearest back do the same, and the third couple likewise. Those at front now take their brooms in right hand. All mark time.

MOVEMENT 8. All face right side of stage, and march to right and up right side of stage. At right back corner leader cuts across to opposite front corner, and others follow. He marches across front of stage, followed by the others. All face front. They hold handle of broom in both hands and let the brush part rest on floor. Music stops and they recite the following together in a very sad tone of voice:

> We are scarecrows;
> We look very dumb.
> We stood in cornfields
> Until we were numb.
> Last spring we frightened
> The black crows away;
> But now we are lonesome
> In the field all day.

[*They shake their heads very sadly and wipe their eyes several times before music continues.*]

MOVEMENT 9. Those at center march backwards. Then those nearest center move backwards until a triangle is formed. Those nearest corners of stage march to center of stage and meet in couples. They march up center of stage until they stand in front of the two at center back. The two at center back step aside, one to each side; the others take their places and face front. Those at side march around outside of lines and come to front corners of stage. The couple that is now second from front march to center front of stage, and turn about and march to back, where they take the place of the couple now at center back of stage. This couple step aside—one to each side. Both march around line to place vacated by those who took their places. The third couple now do likewise. During this entire movement broom is held in both hands directly in front of body.

MOVEMENT 10. Those at front corners of stage come to center front of stage, and in couple formation march toward back of stage. Others follow in couples. At back of stage the first and third couples turn left, while the second and fourth couples turn right. All march down to center side of stage, then to center of stage. When couples meet they face front and march to front, four abreast. The first couple turns to right and the second to left. They march around stage and meet at center back, where those at end of lines back toward back of stage so that a line of eight, facing front, is formed.

MOVEMENT 11. The one at right side of line marches to front left corner, followed by the three nearest him, while the one on left side of line marches to front right corner of stage, followed by the other three. The lines intersect near center of stage. Those at right side of stage march down right side and cut back to form a circle at right side of stage. They continue to march about in circle formation while those on left side of stage do likewise.

MOVEMENT 12. The two nearest back of stage break

circle and go to center back of stage where they meet and come to center front as a couple. The others do likewise. The first couple go to corners and the others fill in the spaces so that a line of eight is formed across front of stage. Music stops and all recite the following in a very sad tone of voice:

> We are scarecrows,
> As sad as can be;
> Our clothes are tattered
> And torn, as you see.
> Still we all know
> Down deep in our hearts,
> That during the spring
> We well do our parts.

[*They nod their heads up and down several times before the music continues.*]

MOVEMENT 13. Beginning with the one nearest the right corner of stage, every other one steps back about four steps. Those in front row face right, and those in back row face left. Those in front row hold the broom in right hand while those in back row hold broom in left hand. All march around stage in the direction which they are facing. They pass at back of stage in train fashion and return to front, still maintaining the double-line formation.

MOVEMENT 14. All mark time in line for eight counts.

All turn to right and face the back of stage. The brooms are then transferred to opposite hand. All repeat the movement above, except that when the lines return to front they form one line across front of stage. Each one steps into place which he originally occupied in line. All hold brooms out in front of body in both hands and mark time for eight counts, shaking their heads from right to left in time with the music.

MOVEMENT 15. The four on right end of line face right, while the others face left. All march around stage in the direction which they are facing. Lines pass in train fashion at back of stage. When the leader of each line reaches back corner of stage, he cuts diagonally across to opposite front corner. Both lines march to center and face front of stage. Here they bow stiffly, turn right, and march off stage.

[*The entire march may be repeated, if desired.*]

THE COMICAL TURKEY PARADE
CHARACTERS
EIGHT TURKEYS, *four boys and four girls*
COSTUMES
TURKEYS: *Masks made of paper.*

MUSIC *and* STEPS: *A slow march may be played. A dragging, listless step is maintained throughout.*

MOVEMENT 1. The four girls enter from right and the four boys enter from left. They swing both arms back and forth as they advance to front of stage in a very haphazard line. All bow to audience, jump into air and click heels together, then bow again to audience.

MOVEMENT 2. The boy and girl at center of stage join hands and skip toward back of stage; pause suddenly near center back, face each other, and hold right hand over heart. The second couple move from center of stage to right side, the third couple to left side, and the last couple remain at front of stage.

MOVEMENT 3. The girls turn to face the right side of stage. Both boys and girls put their hands on their hips. Each girl leads the way in marching in a very small circle around the spot where she has been standing. The boy follows. Thus four small circles are moving about. All pause. Girls turn to face their partners. Partners bow.

MOVEMENT 4. The boys now turn in opposite direction and lead the way about in the same method as before. They pause. Boys turn to face partners, and partners bow to each other.

MOVEMENT 5. Partners lock arms. The couple in right front corner lead the way as all march about stage to the left as couples. Partners look at each other and frequently motion toward each other. They move about the stage in this fashion twice.

MOVEMENT 6. Partners face and bow to each other. They extend and join both hands and move about to right with many slow kicks to the side. Then they move back to left until couples are in original positions. Partners join hands and march around stage to right. They pass around stage once and then return to back. When the first couple reach back left corner, they pause and the others fall in line beside them. Each locks arms with the one next in line. All advance with slow step to front of stage.

MOVEMENT 7. Partners face. Each places left hand on hips and extends right hand toward partner, holding the position for four counts.

MOVEMENT 8. All lock arms with next in line and bow to audience. Then all fold hands in front of chest and recite together in a very monotonous voice:

> Funny, funny, funny, funny,
> Funny turkey folks are we;
> We are funny, funny, funny,
> As you can plainly see.
>
> We make you laugh, laugh, laugh;
> We make you laugh, you see.
> Funny, funny, funny, funny,
> Funny turkey folks are we.

MOVEMENT 9. All face left side of stage and march around stage in that direction, swinging arms back and forth at the sides. When the leader returns to front right corner of stage he cuts to center of stage, where he pauses and marks time. The next three in line follow him and pause so that a line from center extends back to near right front corner. The next four march across stage. At left front corner the leader cuts to center and pauses there, while the others form a line from center to front left corner.

MOVEMENT 10. Those at front corners turn about with both hands on hips as those near center turn about to face front of stage. Those at center march to front of stage. They turn in opposite directions, march around stage, and meet at center back of stage where they face front and mark time. The others mark time in place.

MOVEMENT 11. The next in line then move to center of stage, come to front, march around stage, and take their place beside the first couple while the others mark time. The other couples perform this same movement so that all are in a line across back of stage.

MOVEMENT 12. The four on right side of stage turn toward left, while the four on left side of stage turn toward right. Those on right side step toward front of stage two steps. Then all march around stage in the direction in which they are facing. When the lines meet, they pause and mark time. The leader of the line from the left steps in place between the last two in the line from the right. He turns to face in the same direction as the others.

Movement 13. The others then take their positions, one at a time, in the line from the right and face in proper direction. All march around stage to the right with arms swinging.

Movement 14. When the leader reaches the left back corner of stage, the four at end of line turn around and march in opposite direction. When they reach center of side of stage, both lines turn and march across stage to form a straight line. All lock arms and advance to front of stage. Here they recite the following in a sing-songy tone:

Oh, funny turkey folks we are;
We came here to please you;
We try to make you happy
With the funny things we do.

[All *join hands and take a few kicking steps in place. They then continue with the next verse.*]

We are funny, funny turkeys,
But soon home we must go,
For funny, funny turkey folks
Are busy now, you know.

Movement 15. All turn to right. Place hands on hips of the one in front as all march around stage once. When they return to front of stage they pause, turn to face opposite direction, and march around stage in same fashion.

MOVEMENT 16. All face front, place left hand on hip, hold right hand over heart for a moment, and then extend right hand toward audience. All place both hands on hips, bow to audience, turn left, and march once around stage.

[*Exit* ALL.]

AN AUTUMN QUICKSTEP

CHARACTERS

FOUR GIRLS   FOUR BOYS

COSTUMES

FOUR GIRLS: *White dresses trimmed with streamers of red, green, and gold.* GIRLS *carry sticks wrapped with these colors and decorated with paper turkeys, chrysanthemums, or other symbols of November.*

FOUR BOYS: *Dark trousers, white shirts, and sashes and ties of the red, green, and gold paper. They carry sticks decorated like those of the* GIRLS.

MUSIC *and* STEPS: *Lively music is played for the quickstep.*

MOVEMENT 1. The boys enter from the right and the girls enter from the left of stage. The sticks are swung in the right hand as they enter. From their respective entrances both lines dance to the center front of stage in single file. When the first one in each line reaches the front of stage, he bows to the audience and turns and dances up center of stage to near the back, where he pauses and faces the one from the opposite line. The others do likewise, so that a line of four from right side of stage is facing the line of four from left side.

MOVEMENT 2. Both hands are placed on hips. Sticks are held under right arm. The right foot is put forward and with it the dancers tap time to the music while their heads nod in time. This is continued for a count of eight.

MOVEMENT 3. The boys and girls nearest the back of stage turn toward back of stage, take a few steps in that direction, and then circle about and dance to the center front of stage where they join hands and dance back to line. Each then takes his place on his respective side. The others mark time with head and feet.

MOVEMENT 4. The couples now nearest back of stage repeat the above movement. The next two couples then repeat it in order.

MOVEMENT 5. The boys extend their left hands across their chests and hold their walking sticks erect with the right hand as they step back and bow to the girls, who return their salute by stepping back slightly and curtsying. This movement is repeated. [*The action is lively, in keeping with the music.*]

MOVEMENT 6. Left fists are placed on left hips as all

face front and dance to center front of stage where both lines turn toward sides and dance to opposite front corners, then up side of stage to back corners.

MOVEMENT 7. From back corners lines dance across stage to opposite front corners, lines intersecting at center of stage. From front corners lines dance to center front of stage where they face back and dance diagonally to opposite back corners.

MOVEMENT 8. Lines dance to center back of stage where partners meet, hold walking sticks with their outside hands while they clasp inside hands, and dance to near front of stage where the two lines pause and face each other. The girls curtsy and the boys bow.

MOVEMENT 9. The couple nearest the front step slightly apart, join hands, and raise them high, allowing their walking sticks to point back toward their own shoulders. The remaining girls and boys link arms as they face forward, and in couples dance under arch formed by the first couple. When all the couples have passed under arch, the first couples drop hands, link arms, and dance around after the others into the same formation as before.

MOVEMENT 10. The above movement is repeated with the couple now at the head of the line forming the arch.

MOVEMENT 11. Repeat Movement 10.

MOVEMENT 12. Repeat Movement 10.

MOVEMENT 13. All face front. Inside hands are placed

on hips as the lines dance to front of stage, turn toward their respective sides, and dance to front corners and then around stage to center back.

MOVEMENT 14. When the first couple meet at center back, they clasp hands and dance to front right corner of stage, where they pause. The boy bows and the girl curtsies. The second couple dances to front left corner of stage, the boy bows and the girl curtsies, while the remaining couples go to back corners, doing the same.

MOVEMENT 15. The couples from front right corner and back left corner dance to center of stage where they join hands and dance around in a circle three times to the right. They pause, bow, and curtsy to opposite partners, join hands, and dance about three times to the left. They then bow and curtsy and return to their respective corners. Those who remain in corners during this movement mark time with their toes and keep time with their hands while the others are dancing at center.

MOVEMENT 16. The couples from front left corner and back right corner dance to center of stage and repeat above movement while the others mark time in corners.

MOVEMENT 17. The four girls dance to center of stage, join hands, and dance in a circle three times to right. Then they pause, and each steps back slightly and curtsies to the girl opposite her. All return to their corners.

MOVEMENT 18. The four boys dance to center of stage

and around in a circle, one after another. They dance in a circle to left three times before they pause and each boy bows to the boy opposite. They return to their corners.

MOVEMENT 19. The girls face left and dance to center front of stage while the boys face right and dance to center front. New partners meet at center front and dance up stage to center back, where girls turn to right and dance around stage to center front and boys turn left and dance to center front.

MOVEMENT 20. At center front, partners join hands and dance up stage to form two lines facing each other. Girls step back and curtsy and the boys bow.

MOVEMENT 21. The boy nearest back of stage dances around girls to front of line, where he takes the place of the boy nearest front, who has danced along the line of boys down to the foot of line.

MOVEMENT 22. The boy second from front faces front and dances around the opposite line while the one next to him faces back and dances around the lines in similar fashion. When they return, they exchange places. Thus the original partners are reunited.

MOVEMENT 23. Both hands are placed on hips. The sticks are held in right hand, close to body. All face front and dance toward center front of stage. The first couple remains at center front while the second girl goes to the side of the boy at center and the second boy goes to the side of the girl at center. The others follow suit, so that a line of eight is formed across the front of stage.

MOVEMENT 24. All step back slightly. The girls curtsy to the audience and the boys bow. The two at center of stage turn about, link arms, and dance off stage followed by the other couples.

A THANKSGIVING DAY MOVIE

TIME OF PLAYING: *About fifteen minutes*

CHARACTERS

CHILD

GRANDMOTHER

DUTCH MAIDS, *any number*

PRISCILLA

PURITAN MAIDS, *seven or more*

INDIAN CHIEF

INDIAN BRAVES, *any number*

MILES STANDISH

JOHN ALDEN

PILGRIM MEN, *two or more*

COSTUMES

CHILD: *Usual clothing.*

GRANDMOTHER: *Old-fashioned house dress.*

DUTCH MAIDS: *Typical Dutch dress.*

PRISCILLA *and* PURITAN MAIDS: *Dresses made with long, full skirts and white collars. Pilgrim caps.*

INDIAN CHIEF *and* BRAVES: *Typical Indian dress.*

MILES STANDISH: *Military costume. See page 4 for details.*

JOHN ALDEN *and* PILGRIM MEN: *Short trousers, long stockings, buckles on shoes, etc.*

SCENE: *On one side of stage is a rocking chair. Near by is a low stool or chair. There is a window at one side; an entrance at the opposite side. At the rise of the curtain* GRANDMOTHER *is seated in the rocking chair knitting. The* CHILD *is looking out the window.*

CHILD.

Oh dear! What a gloomy day!
I wish I could go out to play.
But when there isn't any sun,
Well, then, there isn't any fun.

[*Turns around.*]

GRANDMOTHER.

Now, child, don't tease.

CHILD.

But put away your knitting, please.

GRANDMOTHER.

Really, dear, I must not stop.
There, now, you caused a stitch to drop.

CHILD.

I didn't do it—it's this light.

You'll knit until you lose your sight.

GRANDMOTHER.

Oh dear! Oh dear! What shall I do?

CHILD.

I know! I know! And I'll tell you.

Grandmother, tell me just once more

The tale you've told so oft before.

GRANDMOTHER.

But, my dear child, you know it all.

Hark! Didn't I hear Mother call?

CHILD.

Maybe so, but I like to hear.

So tell me again—there, that's a dear—

How the Puritans came across the sea

To America, our country free.

GRANDMOTHER.

All right, my dear, get that big book

And through its pages we will look.

CHILD.

Oh, I know! I know!

Can't we have a picture show?

GRANDMOTHER.

A picture show? That's just the thing!

Each character to us 'twill bring.

CHILD.

So real it seems—we'll have a chance
To hear them talk and see them dance.

GRANDMOTHER.

We must move back; we're much too near
To see the pictures well, I fear.

[GRANDMOTHER *and* CHILD *move chairs to side of stage. Enter* DUTCH MAIDS.]

CHILD.

Little Dutch Maids—the very first thing!
I do hope they will dance and sing.

[*Enter* PURITAN MAIDS *led by* PRISCILLA. *They watch the* DUTCH MAIDS *present the* "Dutch Song and Dance."]

DUTCH SONG AND DANCE

MUSIC: "Where, Oh Where, Is My Little Dog Gone?"

Ve come here tonight
[*Bow, with hand on stomach.*]
Mit a drum and a fife,
[*Pretend to play drum and fife.*]
To sing and to dance you vun song.
[*Hopsy waltz. Right and left four waltz steps.*]
Ve are glad ve are Dutch,
[*Slap chest.*]

You can bet you your life.

[*Shake finger at audience.*]

Mit de English ve don'd get along.

[*Point with thumb over shoulder and shake head.*]

[DUTCH MAIDS *waltz around stage and exit.*]

GRANDMOTHER.

A quaint little dance, quite charming, I'm sure.
See the Puritan maids, so sedate and demure;
They make a very lovely scene
Upon our motion picture screen.

PRISCILLA [*turning to her companions*].

Come, sisters, this must be the way.

SECOND MAID [*looking about sadly*].

Oh dear! Do we have to stay?

THIRD MAID.

America! Land of the free—
I thought the place would fairer be.

FOURTH MAID.

Well, I confess I am surprised.

[*Looks about.*]

'Tis not so grand as I'd surmised.

PRISCILLA.

Sisters all, list thou to me.
Let not thy hearts sore troubled be;

Be not too quick to criticize;
When fault ye find, love often dies.
SECOND MAID.
Thou mayst be right; that I allow.
But I can't help being homesick now.
PRISCILLA.
Wouldst thou return across the sea?
I'm still seasick as I can be!
I'll suffer here, nor once complain;
But I'll not take that trip again.
THIRD MAID.
Priscilla is right; I'll take her stand.
At least we're safe upon dry land.
So let's rejoice—but how, I pray?

[*Pauses.*]

Dancing's a sin, our parents say.
PRISCILLA.
Those maids who dance from Holland came.
Surely *we* might do the same.
The breezes sing through the leafy bowers
And the grasses sway with the dancing flowers.
If God's creatures yield to music's charm,
A little dance can do no harm.

[PURITAN MAIDS *sing, and dance the* "Puritan Maids'
Minuet."]

PURITAN MAIDS' MINUET

Ethelle M. Hermes   Gracelynn Glidden

We'll dance and we'll sing tho' we're Pur - i - tan

maids; We don't wish to   sin, but we're not much a-

fraid. The bir - dies all sing in the trees   o - ver-

head, So it can't be so wrong as our parents have said.

We came to this country our freedom to find
And though we are homesick we really won't mind;
For if we can dance and if we can sing,
Much joy to our lonely hearts the music will bring.

MOVEMENT 1. *Start in couples, inside hands joined
high. Begin with outside foot [i. e., the one away from
partner]. Take three steps [one measure], point inside
foot and hold [one measure]. Repeat two more times,
starting with inside and outside foot [six measures].
Walk daintily on toes and at beginning of each group*

of steps raise the knee slightly and point toe downward. Face partner and curtsy [two measures]. [The curtsy should be little more than a peasant curtsy. Place right foot behind left and bend both knees very modestly.] During this step the four couples should be forming a hollow square, one couple on each side and facing each other at finish.

MOVEMENT 2. *Second step done in place. Join right hands high. Balance forward on right foot [one measure; i. e., step forward on right foot, bring left behind right, rise on toes, and sink]. Balance back [one measure]. Walk around partner with six steps, starting right [two measures]. Balance forward. Balance backward. Face partner lengthwise of hollow square and curtsy.*

MOVEMENT 3. *[To second verse.]*

Here each dancer leaves her partner and passes around square with the following steps, taking two measures to reach each girl.

Three steps and point.

Three steps and curtsy to first girl.

Repeat to second, third, and fourth.

[War whoops off stage. PURITAN MAIDS *end dance abruptly.]*

FOURTH MAID.

Oh sister, pray, what's that I hear?

FIFTH MAID.

Such awful noise fills me with fear!

SIXTH MAID.

We're all alone! Which way is best?

We should have stayed right with the rest.

[*More war whoops off stage.*]

PRISCILLA.

Oh dear! Oh dear! I'm much afraid

We from the rest too far have strayed.

I've oftentimes heard Father tell

How terribly the Indians yell!

Come, let us hide by yonder tree

And make no sound, so quiet be.

[ALL *pretend to hide. Enter* INDIANS.]

INDIAN CHIEF.

Me heap big Injun—ha, ha, ha!

Hear white squaw sing "ta, la, la."

Me find white squaw, take her scalp.

Her no more sing—just yelp.

[INDIANS *dance war dance.*]

SEVENTH MAID [*aside*].

Priscilla dear, what shall we do?

PRISCILLA.

Quiet be, or he'll hear you.

INDIAN CHIEF.

Find white squaw in 'bout a minute.
Make big stew—stick her in it.

[INDIANS *look around.*]

SECOND MAID.

Now I wish I had not come.

THIRD MAID.

What I'd give to be back home!

INDIAN CHIEF [*with wild dance*].

There white squaw—'hind that tree!
Big Chief get her now. Who-ee-ee!

PRISCILLA [*clasps hands in prayer; other* MAIDS *gather round in tears*].

O Heavenly Father, send Thine aid!
Our time has come, we're sore afraid.

INDIAN CHIEF.

White squaw cry—ach, make me sick!

[*Brandishes knife.*]

With heap big knife, me kill 'em quick.

[INDIANS *grab* MAIDS. *Pretend to pull them out from behind tree. Enter* MILES STANDISH, JOHN ALDEN, *and other* PILGRIM MEN.]

MILES STANDISH [*to* INDIAN CHIEF].

What ho! You great big lazy lout,
What's this commotion all about?

Let go thy hold, if thou wouldst live.
About two minutes will I give.

INDIAN CHIEF [*to other* INDIANS].

Bring white squaw here; grab paleface, too.
He no tell Injun what to do.

MILES STANDISH.

Surely, Chief, you do not mean
To be as cruel as it would seem.

INDIAN CHIEF.

Cruel! Bah! Your scalps I'll take.
A heap big string they will make.

JOHN ALDEN.

Oh come! We all must do our best
To help these maidens so distressed.
Priscilla, child! [*To* INDIAN *assailant.*] Let go, my brave.
We've come these maidens' lives to save.

MILES STANDISH.

Come, men, it seems we're just in time
To avert some awful crime.
Now, Chief, come here and be our friend;
To all this trouble put an end.

[*Shows beads.*]

See all the beads—some for your squaw—
If you will just obey the law.
Let these quarrels, these troubles, cease.
Come, let us smoke the pipe of peace.

PILGRIM MEN [*gather round*].
  Yes! O Big Chief, be our friend;
  Please let all this trouble end!
INDIAN CHIEF.
  All right; Big Chief, me good friend.
  Give me beads and fight will end.
  Heap big Injuns dance for you.
  Come on, braves, the Corn Dance do.

  [INDIANS *run off stage and return, each carrying an
  ear of corn and some wood. They use the wood and
  pretend to make a fire. Then they present the* "Indian
  Corn Dance and Harvest Song."]

INDIAN CORN DANCE AND HARVEST SONG

MUSIC: *See opposite page.*

  MOVEMENT 1. *Circle the fire with hop-step, corn in
  hand held high [about eight counts]; step, face fire, hold
  corn high, and bend low, offering corn to fire.*

  MOVEMENT 2. *Every other one take four steps toward
  fire, four steps to turn around, four steps backward to
  place.*

  Others do the same, holding corn high.

  MOVEMENT 3. *Circle the fire again and squat. Shuck
  corn and throw shucks into fire while singing the following song:*

Ethelle M. Hermes   Gracelynn Glidden

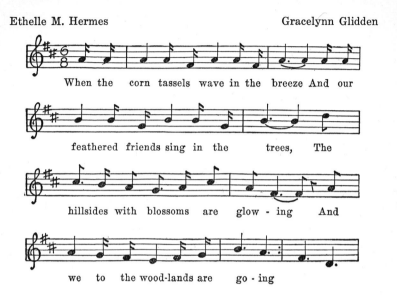

When the   corn tassels wave in the   breeze And our

feathered friends sing in the   trees,   The

hillsides with blossoms   are   glow - ing   And

we   to   the wood-lands are   go - ing

When the autumn winds sigh through the trees
And the woods have soft carpets of leaves,
Indian Corn whose heart is so mellow,
Waves proudly his tassels of yellow.

Then brave youths and fair maidens all
Do answer the gay harvest's call.
With joyous song and with laughter gay
The maize they gather and store away.

At the eventide 'neath starry skies,
When all the world in slumber lies,
We pitch our tents near the rippling stream
And by the glowing campfire dream.

MOVEMENT 4. *After song, rise. Hold corn high. Circle fire again. Stop. Take four steps to fire. Bend low and lay corn on fire. Take four steps to turn around. Take four steps backward.*

MILES STANDISH.

The dance was fine! Now, can't you see
How truly thankful we should be?
Our crops are good, we all are strong,
And, though the winter may be long,
We've food and fuel to last till spring.

PRISCILLA.

Thanksgiving songs of joy we'll sing;
I think 'twould be the nicest way
To have a real Thanksgiving Day.

JOHN ALDEN [*to* PRISCILLA].

To thy plan I will agree,
If thou wilt but Dame Alden be.

PRISCILLA.

O John, how couldst thou be so bold?
Thou wert quite shy, so I've been told.
I feel to thee I owe my life
And I will gladly be thy wife.

MILES STANDISH.

If John had not grown so very bold
I would not be left out in the cold.

But such is life, now sad, now gay.
We'll celebrate Thanksgiving Day
With feast and song; we'll take a chance
And all join in the Harvest Dance.

[*Four couples dance "Harvest Dance." Those not
dancing watch the others and sway in time to the music.*]

HARVEST DANCE

MUSIC: *Any lively march.*

MOVEMENT 1. *Four couples in groups of four, boys
on left. Even numbers in center. All cross hands, join
right hands, and skip around to right [eight skips].
Turn and skip to left [eight skips to four measures].*

MOVEMENT 2. *Even numbers face each other in
two rows. Odd numbers, starting down center, weave
around first two, between them and around second two,
and down center to place [four measures].*

MOVEMENT 3. *Face partners. Balance forward on
right foot; balance backward on left foot. Step on
right, cross left over right, and completely turn right.
Outside four do this four times.*

MOVEMENT 4. *Inside four do the same three times
and turn. Face in and kneel [eight measures]. Repeat
weaving step with center four kneeling. At end they
rise and all step back into circle.*

MOVEMENT 5. *With skipping step do a grand right and left around circle. Dance ends and all join in a song appropriate to the season.*

[*Exit* ALL, *except* CHILD *and* GRANDMOTHER.]

CHILD.

O Grandmother, they've gone away!
I do wish they would longer stay.

GRANDMOTHER.

Your bedtime, child, has long since passed;
Our pleasures cannot forever last.
Some other day, when there's rain or snow,
We'll have another picture show.

CURTAIN

THE THEFT OF THE THANKSGIVING PIE

CHARACTERS

COOK
BOYS *and* GIRLS [*in pumpkin drill*], *four or more*
FOUR HELPERS
FARMER

COSTUMES

COOK: *White cap and apron.*
BOYS *and* GIRLS [*in pumpkin drill*] *and* HELPERS: *Ordinary clothing.*
FARMER: *Overalls and an old hat.*

SCENE: *A table is on the stage. On the table are a pan, a mixing bowl, a spoon, a pie tin with a crust in it, etc. At the side of the stage is a stove on which several pans have been placed, one containing cooked pumpkin. In the oven is a delicious-looking pumpkin pie. At the rise of the curtain,* COOK *stands behind table, ready for work.*

COOK.

> Bring the pumpkin from the field,
> And milk, fresh from the cow;
> It's time to make the pumpkin pie,
> And I will show you how.

[BOYS *and* GIRLS *march in for pumpkin drill. Each carries a pumpkin. During the drill pumpkins may be swung right, left, and overhead, and traded. At end of drill, one pumpkin is placed on table and others on floor around table. Exit* BOYS *and* GIRLS.]

COOK [*cutting pumpkin into pan*].

> All the folks are waiting 'round,
> To taste the pumpkin pie.
> They think it's needed for the feast.
> Indeed, and so do I.

[*Enter* FIRST HELPER, *bringing eggs.*]

FIRST HELPER.

First the pumpkin you should take
And cook it until ready;

[COOK *places pumpkin on stove to cook.*]

Then break the eggs into a dish
And beat them slow and steady.

[COOK *breaks eggs into dish and beats them. Enter* SECOND HELPER, *bringing milk and sugar.*]

SECOND HELPER.

And the milk so fresh and sweet,
With sugar sweeten more.

[COOK *adds milk and sugar. Enter* THIRD HELPER, *bringing spices.*]

THIRD HELPER.

Put in spices for the taste,
And all together pour.

[COOK *puts in spices, then goes to stove for pumpkin. Since cooked pumpkin must be used for pie,* COOK *picks up pan containing that, instead of pan which she put on stove. Pumpkin and other mixture are poured together, and then poured into pie crust. Enter* FOURTH HELPER.]

FOURTH HELPER [*taking pie to oven*].

When the pie is mixed and ready
Place it in the oven—so.

I'm careful not to spill a drop
And I'll turn the fire down low.
[*Stands by stove.*]

[*Exit* FIRST HELPER, SECOND HELPER, *and* THIRD HELPER. COOK *clears table.*]

COOK.

The pie is but a little part
Of this Thanksgiving feast.
The turkey strutting in the yard
Is now a noble beast.

[FOURTH HELPER *takes baked pie from oven and displays it proudly; exits, carrying the pie.*]

I'll get the dressing ready
To stuff in that fat bird;
And then the family'll eat of it
Till they can't say a word.

[*Enter* FOUR HELPERS.]

FOURTH HELPER.

Somebody has taken the pumpkin pie;
I put it on the window shelf.
It must have been a hungry man.
The pie couldn't move by itself.

FIRST HELPER.

There's no one but us on the farm today,
And the cook and the family, too.

I didn't take the pumpkin pie,

[*Looks at* SECOND HELPER, THIRD HELPER, *and* COOK.]

Did you? Did you? Did you?

[*Enter the* FARMER.]

FARMER.

I am the farmer who killed the turkey
And a surprised man am I!
For when I cut him open,
I found the pumpkin pie!

[ALL *laugh.*]

Let's not blame the greedy turkey,
For he will be enough
Served with the potatoes and dressing
And pudding and other "stuff."

[ALL *sing a Thanksgiving song.*]

CURTAIN

THANKSGIVING DAY

CHARACTERS
FIVE CHILDREN

SCENE: *Before the curtain.* CHILDREN *enter in order and stand near the center of the stage.*

FIRST CHILD.

Turkey on the table,
Kith and kin around it—

SECOND CHILD [*interrupting*].
>
> If there's a better day than this
> No one has ever found it!

THIRD CHILD.

> Pumpkin pie a-plenty,
> Squash and corn and yams!

FOURTH CHILD.

> Nuts and cake and candy
> And many kinds of jams!

FIFTH CHILD.

> Games and fun and joking,
> Lots of hearty laughter!

ALL.

> Thanksgiving day is splendid,
> [*Place hands on stomach.*]
> But, oh, the day right after!

THANKSGIVING PIE

CHARACTERS
FOUR CHILDREN

SCENE: *Before the curtain.* CHILDREN *enter in order and stand near the center of the stage.*

ALL.

> As soon as it is sunup
> We will be on our way,
> Because this year, at Grandma's
> We'll spend Thanksgiving Day.

FIRST CHILD.

> The turkey will be sizzling,
> The gravy will be made,
> The cider will be sitting
> Beside the marmalade.

SECOND CHILD.

> The table will be pulled out
> Right to its fullest spread,
> And there'll be in the center
> A bowl of apples red!

THIRD CHILD.

> Grandpa will twist his face up
> In such a funny way,
> And boast the Pilgrim Fathers
> Made our Thanksgiving Day.

FOURTH CHILD.

> But Grandma'll interrupt him
> As he is telling why,
> And say the Pilgrim Mothers
> At least made all the pie.

IN MISTRESS BREWSTER'S KITCHEN

CHARACTERS

PATIENCE BREWSTER, *a girl*
THANKFUL BREWSTER, *a boy*
PERSEVERANCE HOPKINS, *a girl*
HOPE BREWSTER, *a girl*
JOHN BREWSTER, *a boy*
HEZEKIAH CABOT, *a boy*
MISTRESS BREWSTER, *a taller girl*
GOODMAN BREWSTER, *a taller boy*

COSTUMES

PATIENCE BREWSTER, PERSEVERANCE HOPKINS, HOPE
BREWSTER, *and* MISTRESS BREWSTER: *Dark dresses
made with long, full skirts and white collars.*
THANKFUL BREWSTER, JOHN BREWSTER, HEZEKIAH
CABOT, *and* GOODMAN BREWSTER: *Short trousers, long
black hose, buckles on shoes, etc.*

SCENE: *Suggestion of the interior of a Pilgrim cabin.
Entrance at right back. Fireplace at one side. At
center a table on which are several bowls and spoons.
As the curtain rises,* PATIENCE, THANKFUL, PERSEVER-
ANCE, HOPE, *and* JOHN *are discovered standing in a
row facing the audience.*

PATIENCE [*smiling and bobbing a curtsy to the audience*].
          My name is Patience Brewster.
          I came across the sea
          To worship God in freedom
          In this land of liberty.

THANKFUL [*smiling and bowing to the audience*].
          My name is Thankful Brewster.
          I'm a little Pilgrim, too.
          We left our home in England
          Across the ocean blue.

PERSEVERANCE [*frowning at* THANKFUL].
          This land is rough; this sky is cold;
          These woods are dark and thick;
          And many of our Pilgrim folks
          Have mortally been sick.

THANKFUL.
          But don't forget that we've escaped
          The terror and the fear
          That haunted us in England.
          We have free worship here.

HOPE.
          And we have found good treatment
          That we never hoped to find,
          For some of these red Indians
          Have really been kind.

[*Enter* Mistress Brewster *and* Goodman Brewster *from right back.* Mistress Brewster *walks quickly to left front, and the children break their line and cluster at right front, facing her.*]

Mistress Brewster.

Children, why are you standing here?
You're gossiping! And idle, too!

John.

O Mother, we were talking
Of our old homes and our new;
And Perseverance Hopkins says
That we have little store
Of blessings to be thankful for
On bleak New England's shore.

Goodman Brewster [*moving down left to stand beside his wife, facing children*].

For shame! We have our liberty,
Our Bibles, and our lives!
We have our meetinghouse, our homes,
Our children, and our wives!

Patience [*going toward* Goodman Brewster].

Father, why don't we hold a feast
To thank Almighty God
For all His kindnesses to us
Upon this strange new sod?

PERSEVERANCE [*moving up beside* PATIENCE *and looking at her scornfully*].

> A feast? Why, that means meat and drink
> And cakes and pastries, too.
> Where could we find such dainties
> In this country wild and new?

MISTRESS BREWSTER.

> For shame! We have good Indian corn,
> The golden yellow maize;
> And pumpkins have been ripening,
> These pleasant autumn days.

[*Enter* HEZEKIAH CABOT, *right back, holding gun in one hand, and in the other a turkey, or a large sack. He holds up the turkey, or sack, jubilantly, as he strides down to center front.*]

HEZEKIAH.

> Look, here's a turkey that I shot!
> And there were dozens more at least!

GOODMAN BREWSTER.

> I'll go and hunt more turkeys, wife.

ALL OTHERS [*delightedly*].

> Why, what a fine Thanksgiving feast!

[GOODMAN BREWSTER *walks toward the door at right back. At the door he stops and turns toward* MISTRESS BREWSTER.]

And don't you think that some
Of our kind Indian friends
To our big feast should come?

MISTRESS BREWSTER.

Yes, call the Indians.
[*Exit* GOODMAN BREWSTER.]
Children! Children! Children!
You are idle! Never shirk!
Hope, stir the fire.
John, bring more wood.
My daughters, go to work!

[*As the curtain descends,* HOPE *pokes the fire with poker.* JOHN *and* THANKFUL *go out left back. The others move toward the long table and take up bowls and spoons. The curtain is lowered just long enough to permit the entire cast to arrange themselves in a line facing audience, or in a semicircle; when curtain rises again,* ALL *sing first stanza of "America," audience joining in.*]

CURTAIN

THANKSGIVING YEAR BY YEAR
CHARACTERS
NINE CHILDREN

SCENE: *Before the curtain.* CHILDREN *enter in order and stand near the center of the stage.*

FIRST CHILD.

The little Pilgrims of long ago
Had no good times like ours, I know.

SECOND CHILD.

They lived with the English, and then with the Dutch,
But their roving life did not suit them much.

THIRD CHILD.

So, when they heard of our country new,
They sailed over here, though they numbered few.

FOURTH CHILD.

In the ship "Mayflower" they crossed the sea,
To worship God in this country free.

FIFTH CHILD.

In freezing weather they landed here,
And many died that first hard year.

SIXTH CHILD.

But when the first Thanksgiving came,
They had deer meat and other game,

SEVENTH CHILD.

And pumpkin pies and enough food
To fill their hearts with gratitude.

EIGHTH CHILD.

Throughout the feasttime Indians stayed—
Joined in the hunt, and with them played.

NINTH CHILD.
So, to this day, with mirth and cheer,
We keep Thanksgiving year by year.

[*Exit* ALL.]

THREE LITTLE PILGRIM MAIDS

CHARACTERS

SPEAKER
FAITH
HOPE } *three little Pilgrim maids*
CHARITY

COSTUMES

SPEAKER: *Usual clothing.*
FAITH, HOPE, *and* CHARITY: *Typical Pilgrim dress.*

SCENE: *A Pilgrim kitchen. At one side, a fireplace with a pot hanging from crane. Chairs near fireplace. Shining copper and brass kettles around fireplace. A home-made cupboard at one side. Shining pewter plates on shelf; also, wooden plates and mugs and wooden spoons. [If no wooden articles can be obtained, use cardboard plates, etc., from the five-and-ten-cent store.] Table at center. The curtain covers the scene as the* SPEAKER, *standing before the curtain, begins.*

SPEAKER.

Have you ever seen a picture of a colonial kitchen? Of course you have. A huge fireplace! A log that must have been a giant tree of the forest! Wonderful copper and brass kettles! And a good meal in preparation!

And I am going to tell you about three little Pilgrims and the duties they performed in the kitchen of their home. Their names were Faith, Hope, and Charity.

[*Curtain rises, showing the kitchen.*]

Here is the kitchen of the house where the three little maids lived.

It was a winter day and the huge log in the vast fireplace was roaring. Father and Mother would soon be home. Everything must be ready for them.

So into the kitchen hurried Faith to give the stew in the pot a final stir.

[*Enter* FAITH; *stirs the stew.*]

It was really a wonderful stew! Many good things were in it. You see, the Pilgrims raised corn, beans, peas, parsnips, turnips, squash, pumpkins, and other vegetables. For meat they had turkey, venison, wild duck, squirrel, and rabbit. The sea gave them clams, lobsters, and all kinds of fish.

[FAITH *prods fire, then gets a cloth and begins polishing brass kettles and pots.*]

Having attended to the stew and the fire, Faith decided to polish the kettles. How the Pilgrims did love their shining brass and copper! It looked so pretty with the red firelight dancing on it.

Now into the kitchen came Hope. She carried a white linen tablecloth and white linen napkins.

[*Enter* HOPE, *carrying linen. She puts cloth and napkins on table.*]

Perhaps you are surprised that this Pilgrim family had such a fine linen tablecloth. They brought it with them from Holland.

As Hope finished putting the cloth on the table Charity came in and put the dishes on the table. When you say dish you mean something made of china, but when the Pilgrims said dish they meant something made of wood!

[*Enter* CHARITY *with a trayful of plates, mugs, spoons, and knives.*]

The Pilgrims had no china and no glassware. Their plates, mugs, and pitchers were made of wood. It was poplar wood that was used, and when polished and clean it had a shining, white look.

Some of the mugs and pitchers had carvings on them and were very beautiful. Spoons and knives also were made of wood and carved handsomely.

Some of the Pilgrims had pewter, which resembles silver somewhat.

Charity, having put the wooden plates and mugs on the table, now took a pewter plate from the shelf. This plate would hold the bread which the Pilgrims ate, and also cornmeal muffins. Cornmeal muffins were a great favorite with the Plymouth Colony founders.

[*While* CHARITY *sets table,* HOPE *goes out.*]

The table was very attractive, with its white poplar-wood plates and mugs, pewter, and fresh linen. But the day was growing dark. How would the table be lighted?

Hope settled the question. She brought in two tall bayberry candles in candlesticks.

[*Enter* HOPE *carrying candles.*]

Bayberry candles were made from a berry gathered in the fields. When lighted they gave out a lovely perfume that made the whole house smell like a garden.

[FAITH, HOPE, *and* CHARITY *work around the table, straightening plates, etc.*]

Everything was now ready—the table set, the stew cooked, the candles on the table.

[FAITH, HOPE, *and* CHARITY *go to sit beside fire.*]

Faith, Hope, and Charity then sat down by the fire, and waited for their father and mother to come to eat their evening meal.

And now, farewell to three little Pilgrim maids who
lived long ago!

CURTAIN

AUTUMN
Tune: "America"

Dear Autumn, here's to thee,
In beauty rich and free!
Of thee I sing.
Time when the leaves look best,
Time when the fields take rest,
Time when the winds attest
It's Autumntime.

November, here's to thee,
Month very dear to me;
Of thee I sing.
I love your skies of gray,
I love your colors gay,
I love your changeful way,
Dear Autumntime.

WINTER'S WELCOME
Tune: "Solomon Levi," *or* "Harvest Time"

Oh, the time is gay November,
And the frost is in the air;

The cornstalks safely stand in shocks
While the trees are growing bare.
The gardens now are empty,
The birds have flown away;
The chilly little snowflakes
Soon will come this way.

CHORUS

Oh, wintertime is coming,
Tra-la-la-la-la-la-la;
Old jolly wintertime,
Tra-la-la-la-la-la-la-la-la.

The apples red are put away,
The grain is in the barn;
A hazy sort of atmosphere
Rests over every farm.
The summer days are missing,
The autumn is passing by;
The air is crisp and snappy
For soon the snow will fly.

NOVEMBER, THE BEAUTIFUL
Tune: "America, the Beautiful"

O beautiful for gorgeous woods,
For streams so cold and clear,

For bittersweet and gay sumac,
And all we hold most dear.
November, November,
God greatly has blest you,
And crowned thy ways with happy days
And good in all you do.

O beautiful for healthful hours,
For fragrant morning air,
For vineyards royally laden down,
And pumpkins great and fair.
November, November,
I bless your every hour;
A king's ransom would not replace
The things within your power.

NOVEMBER NIGHT

Tune: "Stars of the Summer Night," *or* "Arbor Day"

Stars of November night,
How bright you shine on high!
Shed, shed your golden light
O'er all the azure sky.
Shine bright! Shine bright!
O stars on high.

Moon of November night,
Light up the world below;
Shine, shine, your little beams,
Each child loves to know;
Shine on, shine on,
With lovely glow.

Breeze of November night,
Blow gently o'er me;
Kiss with your cooling breath
Each ruffly leaf you see.
Blow on, blow on!
Blow on for me!

OUR PILGRIMS
Tune: "Auld Lang Syne"

1. Should all the Pilgrims be forgot,
And all their loyal men;
A brilliant page of history
We would be lacking then.

CHORUS

In honor of our Pilgrims, then,
We sing words of praise;
We'll praise them with both word and song
Through all Thanksgiving Days.

2. Should Plymouth Rock e'er be forgot,
   And "Mayflower" brushed away,
   Our memories would be less dear
   On each Thanksgiving Day.

CHORUS

But thankful are we it's not so,
For we remember well
The deeds of Pilgrims strong and brave,
Of whom we've oft heard tell.

TURKEY TALK

Tune: "Comin' Thro' the Rye"

1. If a turkey meet a turkey,
   Near Thanksgiving Day;
   If a turkey greet a turkey,
   What does turkey say?

CHORUS

Every turkey has its trouble,
When Thanksgiving's near;
And every turkey's sure to feel
He'll lose his head, I fear.

2. If a gobbler meet a gobbler
   In the barnyard lane,
   He'll shake his head and gobble then
   As if in awful pain.

CHORUS